MEDITATIONS FOR SURVIVING

WITHOUT CIGARETTES

Esther Wanning

AVON BOOKS · NEW YORK

MEDITATIONS FOR SURVIVING WITHOUT CIGARETTES is an original publication of Avon Books. This work has never before appeared in book form.

AVON BOOKS
A division of
The Hearst Corporation
1350 Avenue of the Americas
New York, New York 10019

Copyright © 1994 by Esther Wanning
Cover illustration by Albert Drogin
Interior design by Suzanne H. Holt
Published by arrangement with the author
Library of Congress Catalog Card Number: 93-29460
ISBN: 0-380-76916-6

Library of Congress Cataloging in Publication Data:

Wanning, Esther.
  Meditations for surviving without cigarettes / Esther Wanning.
    p.   cm.
  1. Cigarette habit.   2. Cigarette smokers—Rehabilitation.
3. Self-help techniques.   4. Meditations.   I. Title.
HV5740.W36   1994   93-29460
613.85—dc20   CIP

First Avon Books Trade Printing: January 1994

AVON TRADEMARK REG. U.S. PAT. OFF. AND IN OTHER COUNTRIES, MARCA REGISTRADA, HECHO EN U.S.A.

Printed in the U.S.A.

OPM   10   9   8   7   6   5   4   3   2   1

Welcome to the majority. Only 26 percent of adult Americans

smoke, and they nearly all wish they didn't. Public opinion holds smokers in low esteem. When a person lights up a cigarette, others see a poor soul lacking in self-control, a victim. To put it unkindly, a drug addict. After all, precious few people smoke because they want to. They smoke because they can't stop. Yet they are surrounded by people who could stop and did. How does that make them feel?

Bad. As you did until today. Now you have crossed to the other side. You can hold up your head. You can sit in the no-smoking section. You don't have to subject yourself to other people's whims by asking the sniveling question "Mind if I smoke?" Now you're as good as they are.

Twenty minutes after your last cigarette, nicotine ceased to affect your blood pressure, pulse, and body temperature. Within eight hours, the carbon monoxide level in your blood drastically fell, and increased oxygen is now reaching all the tissues of your body.

❖   ❖

"I admit that like all born-again nonsmokers, I look down on those who are still hooked."

—*Art Buchwald*

| D A Y   2 | Don't feel sorry for yourself. People moan about the pain of

quitting, but what about the pleasure? Things are looking up already. You've cleared out those vile ashtrays. You smell better. You don't have to look for your cigarettes.

You probably don't feel your best today. You crave a cigarette, naturally. You expected that. But you may also be bowed down by headaches, nausea, sweatiness, aches, and digestive upsets. Not to mention irritability, restlessness, anxiety, and difficulty concentrating. These are normal nicotine withdrawal symptoms, and they pass quickly. You can ignore them, or if you prefer, declare yourself sick and go to bed. It's best to stay away from smokers; this is a perfect time to haunt museums, movie theaters, parks, and mountain trails. One woman spent the first two no-smoking days on her bicycle, miserable and depressed. On the third day she felt wonderful.

Withdrawal is a nasty business. Wouldn't care to repeat it, would you? Even if you're on a nicotine patch, you're unlikely to be feeling wholly yourself. Observe your feelings, as if they were a passing parade. They will retreat, and so will the urge for a cigarette, unless you smoke. Tomorrow will be different.

TODAY'S TIP: *When a craving to smoke comes over you, take three deep slow breaths. Hold the third as long as you can.*

You have conferred tremendous benefits on yourself by

quitting smoking. You've added not just eight years (on average) to your expected life span, but eight much healthier years
than you could look forward to as a smoker. Put to good use,
they will be far happier years, too. You are now in a position
to get more out of life than you ever could as a smoker. That
cloud of smoke stood between you and life's full experience.

At the moment you may be coughing or clearing your throat
more than ever before—so much so that your chest may hurt.
Be glad. You've recovered the ability to clear out blocked airways, which were stuck full of mucus. The clearing-out process
lasts only a few days, and your old smoker's cough (the body's
attempt to protect itself from the irritants in cigarette smoke) will
be history in a few weeks.

Fatigue during the day and wakefulness at night are normal
withdrawal symptoms, not likely to last more than a few weeks.
Intestinal upsets can also last weeks, but most of your other
symptoms will pass in a day or two. The worst cigarette cravings should now be behind you.

❖ ❖

*"If you have the will to change, quitting smoking doesn't
have to be hard. Don't be afraid."*
                                    —ETHAN RUTHERFORD, *ex-smoker*

| D A Y 4 | Your worst physical withdrawal symptoms should have passed

by now. If the only reason you smoked was that you'd once had the bad luck of becoming addicted to nicotine, you'd be home free.

But people are not such fools that they smoke out of addiction alone. They smoke because smoking is rewarding. Chances are, you have a number of hurdles still to cross in your metamorphosis into a nonsmoker. In the past, smoking has helped you to regulate your moods, ignore pain, control excitement, ward off anxiety, and medicate depression. But as smoking provides only a distraction, not a cure, smokers tend to have a lot of unfinished business in their psyches.

When someone stops smoking, he or she is apt to suffer most from the intensity of emotions. The uplifting ones can be as intimidating as the anxious ones. Both scream "Cigarette!" The trick is to let these feelings rush by without succumbing to them. In time, you will learn to tend your emotions far more effectively without cigarettes than you ever did with them.

❖ ❖

"Whenever possible, the patient should spend two or three weeks in a sanitarium while learning to get along without the drug [tobacco]."

—JOHN HARVEY KELLOGG, M.D.,
Tobaccoism or How Tobacco Kills, *1929*

As long as you smoked, your body operated under a tremendous hindrance. It had to adapt not only to nicotine, but to the 4,000-plus other chemicals found in burning tobacco (over 40 of which are known to be carcinogenic).

| D A Y 5 |

That smoke that you took in didn't just gum up your lungs but passed immediately into your bloodstream. The carbon monoxide in the smoke displaced oxygen, making you tired and breathless. Nicotine sped up your heart rate and raised your blood pressure. When you lit a cigarette your body temperature also fell, and less blood flowed to your arms, legs, and feet. If you're feeling tingling now in your fingers and toes, it's because you're noticing improved circulation.

If you still want a cigarette, try the 4 D's: Drink water, Delay, Deep-breathe, Do something else. The craving will go away in a couple of minutes—if you don't smoke.

Rx: Quit: Smokers get sick much more often than nonsmokers. The gases in tobacco injure the tissues of the lungs and the airways to them. As a result, extra mucus is produced and the lungs become a fertile breeding ground for colds, flu, pneumonia, and bronchitis.

You do exercise, don't you? Exercise lets you fully reap the sense of well-being that comes from not smoking. Exercise does well what smoking does badly, which is to alleviate anxiety, depression, and restlessness. Both smoking and exercise give the brain's neurotransmitters a boost, but the effects of exercise are much longer lasting. A cigarette produces only a few minutes' reprieve from anxiety; a good workout creates genuine relaxation, lasting hours. For those who worry about getting fat, exercise is a critical part of the program.

It's necessary to find an exercise you can bring yourself to do regularly. You can hate running and still like ice skating or racquetball or weight lifting or bicycling or swimming or yoga. Good old walking will do fine. An easy stroll is far better than nothing.

In your early weeks of not smoking, you should try for at least one exercise break a day. The exertion cuts the craving for a cigarette, and there is satisfaction in making the most of your body's growing capabilities—now that it is no longer a smoking machine.

❖ ❖

A MAN OF HONOR: In 1922, a tobacco company tried to get heavyweight champion Jack Dempsey to sign a testimonial. "I can't sign that," said Dempsey. "I wouldn't do it for ten times what you offer. I don't smoke, and I never did."

"Just for today" is a key slogan in Nicotine Anonymous: "Just

for today, I will not smoke." You may reassess the situation tomorrow, whereupon you may decide to smoke again. Thus, your only problem is getting through today. In the years to come, if you want to smoke, say to yourself, "Well, maybe tomorrow." Tomorrow, one hopes, you will decide you can get through tomorrow. This takes the chill off making a lifetime decision. The thought of forever may be too much to contemplate. And if tomorrow seems too close to forever, there's "Just for the next seven minutes I will not smoke."

❖ ❖

"But I would have thee remember that if thou shoulds't become a non-smoker, it will be because thou hadst decided for thyself . . . for every man has a free will to accept or reject tobacco unless it has, by its very nature, taken such a hold on him as to compel him to make a choice in its favour."

—A. A. WILLIAMS, **A Smoker's Pilgrim's Progress**, 1922

| D A Y   8 | Congratulations. Your first and worst week without cigarettes

is over. It is not, however, time to relax your vigilance. Instead, count your blessings. You look better, you smell better, and you're welcome wherever you go. You are probably enjoying your food more, too. Few great cooks are smokers, as smokers generally lack both the passion for food and the nose for it. You may, however, now be demonstrating an obsession with food that you'd rather not have, and you should take certain precautions.

If you crave sweets, suck on lemon drops or Life Savers. Bowls of sunflower seeds around the house are diverting. Keep plenty of fruit, juice, and ice water on hand, and fill the fridge with ready-to-eat vegetable snacks. You can use the vitamins; as a smoker, you needed more and absorbed less. And eat good square meals, remembering that the U.S. government recommends that we all eat five to seven servings of fruit and vegetables each day. This is no time to diet. Chew gum if you must, but bear in mind that some people find gum chewing even more irritating than smoking.

❖   ❖

"If you want to stop smoking, you have to be prepared to change your life."

—SALLY T., *ex-smoker*

Even though he quit 16 years ago, Michael Mery vividly remembers how difficult it was. "I loathed myself for smoking, for trashing myself, but it still took me a long time to quit. When I finally did stop, the first three days were just the normal physical withdrawal. Then a lightheadedness set in that was so extreme that I was borderline dangerous [Mery is a carpenter and works with power tools]. At the same time, I was almost euphoric not to be smoking.

"I'd also break out in a sweat from head to foot while just sitting in a chair, and I had major joint pain. I was irritable for months. Three months after I quit I had a drag of my then-wife's cigarette. Having that one drag filled me with fury at myself for being so stupid. That was the last time I smoked.

"I didn't notice much physical change until one day I was shoveling horse manure into my truck for my mother's garden. I was in a big hurry, and I loaded up in less than twenty minutes. As I drove away I was amazed to notice that I wasn't winded. Now I run twenty miles a week. I'm just grateful to be free of cigarettes."

❖ ❖

"A lot of working guys have been smoking for so long that they have no idea how much stamina they have lost."
—MICHAEL MERY, *ex-smoker*

```
┌─────────────────────┐  Day by day, this book takes
│   D A Y   1 0   │  note of the milestones the ex-
└─────────────────────┘
```
smoker passes along the road to recovery. Some body parts re-
cuperate quickly, some slowly. For ease of reference, we
collect together here some of the highlights in the progress of
an ex-smoker.

Twenty minutes after the last cigarette: Blood pressure,
pulse, and body temperature return to normal.

Eight hours later: Carbon monoxide level in the blood falls,
allowing oxygen level to rise.

Seventy-two hours later: The bronchial tubes relax, and
breathing becomes easier. The lung power increases. Coughing decreases.

Two weeks to three months: Circulation improves; stamina
increases; lung capacity increases up to 30 percent.

Two months: Chronic cough completely disappears.

One to nine months: Sinus congestion, fatigue, and shortness of breath decrease. The cilia regrow in the lungs.

One year: Risk of heart disease falls to half that of a current
smoker.

Five years: Risk of heart attack and stroke almost equals that
of a never-smoker.

Six years: Risk of bladder cancer becomes half that of a
never-smoker.

Ten years: Risk of lung cancer drops to half that of a never-
smoker.

Fifteen years: Risk of lung cancer drops to almost that of a
never-smoker.

❖ ❖

FACT: *When you smoke a single cigarette, the recovery reverses.*

Chances are that you still feel a
berserk craving for a cigarette

from time to time. Even nonbelievers may take recourse in
prayer at such moments. Saying "God help me" (while breathing deeply) comes as naturally to quitters as it does to drowning sailors. Both are, after all, fighting for their lives.

Leo Tolstoy, author of *War and Peace*, felt that people
smoked, or took other intoxicants, to drown the conscience. He
gives as an example the cook who cut his lady's throat but
could not finish her off until he smoked a cigarette. Thieves,
gamblers, and prostitutes nearly all smoke—and so do people
in lawful professions, says Tolstoy, if their behavior requires
them to quiet their consciences.

❖   ❖

*"It is assumed that tobacco cheers one up, clarifies one's
thoughts, and attracts people toward itself like any other
habit, without ever producing that effect of drowning
the conscience which is recognized in the case of wine.
But one need but look more attentively at the conditions
in which a special necessity for smoking is manifested,
in order to become convinced that the intoxication by means
of tobacco, like that by means of wine, acts upon the
conscience, and that men consciously have recourse to this
intoxication."*
—*Leo Tolstoy*, **Why People Become Intoxicated**, *1890*

| D A Y   1 2 | Most smokers cling to the odd idea that cigarettes reduce

stress. In fact, the effect of smoking is quite the opposite. On lighting a cigarette, the pulse speeds up, blood pressure increases, and the heart pumps faster. The smoker may enjoy a moment's tranquility when the nicotine hits the brain, but that is quickly followed by the agitation of withdrawal. So the next cigarette quickly follows, sending a further volley of toxins into the body and to the nervous system. The upshot is that smoking is the world's worst way to cope with stress.

Rx for stress: Take three deep breaths and hold the last one as long as you can. Have a hot bath. Run around the block. Do some stretches. Envision snowcapped mountains. Find someone pleasant to talk to. Pour out your soul into a notebook. Go to bed early.

❖ ❖

"Smoking is a custom loathsome to the eye, hateful to the nose, harmful to the brain, dangerous to the lungs, and in the black stinking fume thereof, nearest resembling the horrible Stigian smoke of the pit that is bottomless."
—JAMES I OF ENGLAND, 1604

Coffee drinking and smoking
go together in the minds of

many smokers like the proverbial horse and carriage—so much so that some cigarette quitters feel they must renounce coffee also. But adding the stress of giving up coffee to that of giving up cigarettes can be unduly traumatic. Most cigarette quitters would just as soon postpone caffeine withdrawal, perhaps till the grave.

However, you might be well advised to cut down on the quantity of caffeine you're taking in. Smokers metabolize caffeine faster than nonsmokers. In one test, caffeine levels went up 46 percent after smokers quit smoking—while still drinking the same amount of coffee. This could account for some of the irritability and nervousness attributed to cigarette withdrawal.

So add some decaf to your usual coffee brew, and if need be, alter your rituals. The after-breakfast cup of coffee causes many recent ex-smokers to grieve for their after-breakfast cigarettes. Have that second cup of coffee (maybe decaf) but don't sit around with it. Stroll in the garden. Strum the old guitar you've stowed in the closet. And this is an excellent time to write in your journal—where you can express those feelings you're no longer trying to extinguish with smoke.

❖ ❖

"When someone smokes, what I see is a person inhaling his feelings."

—MICHAEL PARMELEY, *never-smoker*

```
 D A Y   1 4
```
Two weeks smoke free! You're feeling like a real nonsmoker now, not even thinking about cigarettes for big chunks of time. You may still have bad moments, very likely in the evenings when you're tired and your defenses are low. It's a good idea to acquire new routines to get your mind off sinking into an easy chair with a cigarette. One couple who quit together now each evening take a stroll together.

You may need to find things to do with your hands: Set up a picture puzzle, do the ironing, bake bread, groom the dog, sew, take up needlework, make a model airplane, pull weeds, or practice your golf swing. One ex-smoker started making a replica of the Vatican from a cut-out book. "It's incredibly soothing," she says. "I methodically cut, fold, and glue, and the Vatican rises before me."

Michelangelo didn't smoke. If he had, at the age of eighty he could hardly have been hanging from the Vatican's Sistine Chapel ceiling painting the frescoes.

❖   ❖

"No possible claim can be made for cigarettes as enhancers of life on any level. The solace they provide is a spurious one, since they merely quell the pangs of an insatiable addiction created by one of their pharmacological components, nicotine."

—WILLIAM STYRON, The Nation, 1987

Irritability is a big complaint of people who quit smoking. All

those little things that you once took in your stride bug you. The sound of certain voices may make you feel murderous. Being put on hold is more than you can take. Trying to be civil is exhausting. You miss the old easygoing Joe or Jill everybody was so fond of; anything that got on your nerves was met with a cigarette.

You can be fairly confident that your irritability level will go down in the next two weeks, although you may not become like Buddha. It's possible that behind that curtain of smoke, which you raised whenever any small annoyance was at hand, is a somewhat irritable person, and one of the reasons you smoked was to obscure that unwelcome fact. Becoming less irritable, which you can do, may take some time and effort—with meditation, therapy, fresh air, biofeedback, exercise, etc.

There are, however, some things that are just plain irritating, such as injustice and dishonesty. These should rightfully be met with action, rather than with either smoking or a smile.

❖   ❖

"One of the worst effects of smoking is that it deadens our susceptibility to tedium, and enables us to keep on enduring what we ought to war against and overcome."
    —JAMES PARTON,
        Does It Pay to Smoke and Drink? *1877*

DAY 16

It helps to practice turning down cigarettes before the chance even arises. Imagine Rhett Butler sidling up next to you while you're standing in line at the movies. "Cigarette?" he says. "NO THANK YOU. I DON'T SMOKE," you say. Rhett won't stick around, but you could be stuck with the cigarettes for years to come.

Suppose something frightening happens. Your brother is out fishing, there's a storm, his boat doesn't return. You are waiting at the pier with your sister-in-law, who is chain-smoking. DON'T SMOKE. Whatever happens, smoking will only make it worse.

Actually, it's usually the mundane situations that get you. Your cousin, a nonstop talker who has been boring you out of your skull for 25 years, is visiting. In a moment of clarity, you realize that chain-smoking got you through his visits before. Get out your knitting. Or get him out. If a situation is driving you to smoke, change the situation.

❖ ❖

"Smoking is just a terrible, dirty habit ... It was once glamorous, but now it is a nuisance and one that no longer interests me."

—GLENN FORD, *actor and ex-smoker*

A smoker is a slave, at the beck and call of a cigarette.

You, however, are now free. As your life need no longer be arranged around smoke breaks, you can go anywhere and do anything. If you've dreamed of exploring interior New Guinea, you can go without worrying about running out of cigarettes. And speaking of running, you don't get that awful pain deep in your lungs anymore when you dash for a bus. If you're lucky, you stopped smoking before you had a heart attack.

Young persons who have heart attacks are overwhelmingly smokers. The chemicals in tobacco accelerate arteriosclerosis, and the hearts of smokers are starved for oxygen. Carbon monoxide, inhaled from tobacco, readily displaces oxygen in the bloodstream. A smoker has 8 to 30 times as much carbon monoxide in his or her veins as a nonsmoker—thus getting less oxygen than a nonsmoker would at 8,000 feet.

Young males who smoke two packs a day have seven times the risk of a heart attack as nonsmokers. For young women—under age 50—smoking two packs a day raises the risk for heart attack to ten times that of nonsmoking women.

❖ ❖

AN EARLY GRAVE: A. Bartlett Giamatti, who left the presidency of Yale University to become the commissioner of baseball, died suddenly of a heart attack at age fifty-one. He was a heavy smoker.

| D A Y 1 8 | Has anyone commented on how much better you smell?

There are no two ways about it: smokers stink. One can usually detect a smoker by smell alone, and stale tobacco is not an endearing odor. A smoker's house stinks, too. Most of us do not care to hang around inside one. Often it's also overheated because the smoker has poor circulation and jacks the thermometer up. The smell inside a smoker's car does not bear mention.

❖ ❖

"What I hated most about being a smoker was opening my locker at the gym after a shower. I'd be feeling terrific from playing racquetball, and then this terrible stale odor of tobacco would come whooshing out from my street clothes. It was disgusting, and I knew it."
—SUZANNE MANTELL, *ex-smoker*

Another aesthetic considera-
tion: wrinkles. Women espe-

cially wrinkle up from smoking, probably because of a lack of
blood flow to the skin. One study of smokers and wrinkling,
based on photographic portraits, concluded that smokers ages
40 to 49 had as many wrinkles as nonsmokers 20 years older.

The coloring of a smoker isn't pretty either. Likewise due to
lack of blood circulation, the skin tends to be sallow, lacking
that slight blush that adds to sex appeal. No amount of
makeup substitutes for moist, dewy skin. You probably already
look far better than you did twelve days ago.

Men have tougher skin, but men who smoke are still far
more likely to be excessively wrinkled than nonsmokers. Smoking certainly undermines the virile look, and a smoking man
looks more beaten than bold. And in time, the health problems
associated with smoking do their sad work. Nobody who is
carrying an oxygen bottle looks sexy.

❖ ❖

*"Not many doctors would do a face-lift on someone who
smoked. Wounds don't heal as well, and face-lifts are especially
delicate as you've separated the skin from most of the
blood supply."*

—DR. JEFFREY BINSTOCK, *cosmetic surgeon*

| D A Y 2 0 |

Besides the smell and the wrinkles, another giveaway that someone is a smoker is stained, yellow teeth. Young people may escape tobacco-colored teeth for a while, but eventually the effects catch up with them.

Smokers get four to five times more gum disease than non-smokers and are more likely to lose their teeth at an early age. A study of 17,000 people in Buffalo, New York, revealed that the condition of the gums and underlying bones of smokers was comparable to that of nonsmokers fifteen years older. Among women with osteoporosis, the smokers are three times more likely to lose their teeth than the nonsmokers.

Now's the time to make an appointment for a teeth cleaning to get the old cigarette stains off. Your teeth should look a lot better afterward and will stay that way if you don't smoke. If there's irreversible damage, you might want to look into the new staining and bonding processes.

❖ ❖

"Smokers' teeth are very hard to clean. Sometimes I can't get all the stains off in one appointment, although I tell smokers to come in every three months. Over the years, tobacco soaks into the teeth and yellows them permanently. I can tell if people once were heavy smokers even after they've quit."

—CAROL SCHATZBERG, *dental hygienist*

Nicotine Anonymous is a fast-spreading program. Like Alco-

holics Anonymous, it is based on twelve steps, it has no dues or fees, and meetings are run by unpaid members. Sabrina P. has been attending meetings weekly for the two years since she stopped smoking.

❖ ❖

"I'd tried everything by the time I got to Nicotine Anonymous. The support and awareness I found there are the reasons I'm not smoking today. I had to realize that I'm an addict. That's the baseline. People at meetings said, 'Don't listen to your brain, except for entertainment, because it's addicted.' I had been smoking two packs a day for thirty years. Who knew what this person was like without a drug?

"Cigarettes had been my higher power. They regulated my life. I preferred smoking to sex. When I smoked, I never felt alone because I had my cigarettes. When I put my cigarettes down I couldn't stand the gaping hole inside. I felt I was one of those smokers who would smoke through the hole after a tracheotomy. It's a miracle that I stopped. I prayed, I worked in my garden for six hours nonstop, I stood in my living room and screamed. People at meetings would say that if you're going to stop smoking you have to be prepared to change your life. I was and I did. I'm not just healthier. I'm calmer, I have self-esteem, and my relationships are far better. Smoking kept me shame-based, a word I picked up from John Bradshaw. I'm not shame-based anymore."

—SABRINA P., ex-smoker

| DAY 22 | If you're still having strong impulses to smoke (or worse, succumbing to the impulses), keep track of what brings up the urge. Parties are hard for a lot of people. It may help if you break the ice when you arrive at a party by announcing immediately to somebody that you've quit smoking. After that, most people find it too humiliating to be seen with a cigarette. If that doesn't work, lay off parties for a while. Not smoking is more important.

The liquor at parties adds to an ex-smoker's vulnerability. If drinking makes you smoke, then drinking may have to go. And if you can't stop drinking, you have a drinking problem. Call Alcoholics Anonymous or the National Council on Alcoholism.

❖ ❖

"Whenever Yul [Brynner] and I met, I would plead with him to quit. . . . We met for the last time at Memorial Sloan-Kettering Hospital, 36 years after our first introduction. Yul was in a wheelchair, on his way to radiation therapy for painful lung cancer metastases in his spine . . . as he was being wheeled away, he looked back at me, shook his head, and said, 'Why the hell didn't I listen to you?' "
—WILLIAM G. CAHAN, M.D., **No Stranger to Tears**, 1992

The American obsession with thinness has the tragic effect of

keeping many people hooked on cigarettes. It's all very well for doctors to say that you could gain 100 pounds and still be healthier than if you smoked. Given the choice, you'd rather be dead.

There is a fair chance that you are going to end up weighing more than you did while you smoked, but probably not by much. It appears that smoking lowers your natural weight—setpoint—and so when you stop, the body perceives itself as underweight. Consequently, you may suddenly find yourself eating like a horse. The important thing is not to panic and imagine that you're going to go on eating like a horse indefinitely. Once the body reaches its new chosen weight, your appetite will drop off.

A few people do add considerable poundage, which can take a few years to deal with, but a fair number of people do not gain weight at all. Exercise, like smoking, seems to lower the body's setpoint, as well as transforming belly fat to muscle.

❖ ❖

WHAT PRICE VANITY?: Babe Paley, the beautiful wife of CBS president William Paley, smoked. "If I quit, I'll get fat," she said. She developed lung cancer.

"Smoking kept her weight down all right," Dr. William Cahan writes. "Within a year, she developed painful metastases that reduced her to skin and bones. I'm told that her beauty became even more haunting as her cheekbones were accentuated and her dark eyes shone luminously through her pallor, until they were dulled by narcotics—and death."

| D A Y   2 4 |

The life of a smoker has become particularly miserable in recent years now that many households are hostile to smoking. A visit with friends entails suffering for the smoker. While others are making merry, the smoker is longing for a cigarette. She becomes more and more distracted as the question looms larger: When can she make a break for it? Just as she's about to pop into the garden for a cigarette, dinner is served. After dinner, when it would seem reasonable to have a little smoke outdoors, some bore is telling an endless story, and she can't politely exit until it's finished. And then soon after she's served her addiction, the old urge starts all over again.

It's just as bad in restaurants. Even understanding friends may admit that smelling smoke while they're eating makes them sick. Smoking was certainly more fun when there was a happy conviviality about it. Now, a person who unveils a pack of cigarettes feels like a murderer.

❖ ❖

"I quit because smoking had become socially impossible."
—RUTH WATT, ex-smoker

In your first few weeks as a nonsmoker, your sleep may be

D A Y   2 5

disturbed, but you may soon be sleeping more soundly than you did before, particularly if you've been getting some exercise. You may find yourself needing more sleep than you used to (you're more active during the day) or less (you have more energy). Don't get overtired, which leads to carelessness, which leads to smoking.

Meanwhile, keep a good book next to your bedside and be glad you don't have to worry about falling asleep with a cigarette in your hand. In Baltimore, a three-year study found that more than half the house fires were caused by smoking. Of those who died, 39 percent were not the smokers themselves.

❖ ❖

NEWS ITEM: *"A San Anselmo woman died Sunday after she apparently fell asleep on her couch while smoking. . . . When firefighters arrived, the front window had blown out and the front door was open as if neighbors had tried to get the woman out, but were forced back by smoke and heat. [Eleanor] Hendricks, who lived alone, was found dead inside the home."*

—The Marin Independent Journal,
[*California*] *April 27, 1991*

Although cigarettes have been the downfall of most contemporary tobacco addicts, there are other ways to go—pipes, cigars, snuff, chewing tobacco. In India there's the problem of reverse chutta smoking—which is the smoking of a cigarlike stick with the lit end inside the mouth.

The practitioners of these minority methods should not imagine that they are exempt from the problems of cigarette smoking. While the mortality statistics are highest for cigarettes, each method of nicotine intake has its own nasty side effects. Pipe smokers have high rates of lip and pharynx cancer; cigar smokers get tongue cancer; and snuff and chewing tobacco lead to tongue and gum cancer and heart disease. Furthermore, all nicotine users are drug addicts and consequently to some degree are escaping reality and operating beneath capacity.

If your problem was tobacco, but not cigarettes, just substitute the name of your habit when reading this book. Be assured that your vice, whatever it was, was just as vile as cigarettes.

❖　❖

It's a Fact: Danish men who smoke cheroots (small cigars) have heart attack rates four times greater than nonsmokers and twice as great as cigarette smokers, according to a seven-year study of 5,000 men.

Among smoking diseases, lung cancer is one of the quicker

ways to go. Emphysema is one of the lingering ones. The air sacs of the lungs are destroyed; by the time the disease is diagnosed a large percentage of these sacs are gone. The sufferer may be left struggling for breath for years before death comes. Smokers have ten times the emphysema rate of nonsmokers.

Even in the early years of smoking, tobacco is inflicting permanent damage on the lungs. Damaged lungs cannot be reconstituted, but fortunately one can breathe with lungs that operate way below capacity. If the damage is arrested, one may be lucky enough to never seriously suffer from the harm already done.

❖ ❖

"I have oxygen coming into my lungs 24 hours a day through the plastic tubes inserted in my nostrils. I shouldn't complain. I can afford portable oxygen, so that if I can muster up the energy, I can walk to other parts of the house. My less-fortunate, lower-ranking shipmates who have come down with emphysema can't afford the luxury of a home 'wired for oxygen,' so to speak. They are in VA hospitals by the thousands, sometimes confined to their beds with wall oxygen outlets ... Chained to their beds, they live out their days in an agony worse than pain—air hunger."

—REAR ADMIRAL GERALD E. SYNHORST,
Saturday Evening Post, 1986

DAY 28

It may seem surprising that the simple act of smoking can cause such varied damage to remote areas of the body. The explanation is that tobacco smoke is made up of a wide variety of toxic chemicals that circulate through the entire body in the bloodstream. Carbon monoxide is only one of the more deadly chemicals produced.

Nicotine itself is the usual suspect when it comes to raising blood pressure and forming blood clots, but it's the other chemicals that cause cancer. More than forty have been identified as carcinogens, and some are complete carcinogens, capable of starting tumors single-handedly. One is beta-naphtylamine, which causes bladder cancer, a cancer seven to ten times more common in smokers than in nonsmokers. Wherever tar lands in the system, it produces abnormal cells, which is where cancers start. For pipe and cigar smokers who don't inhale, the main cancer sites are the lips, tongue, mouth, jaws, larynx, and esophagus. For cigarette smokers, the primary list goes on to include the lungs, bladder, kidneys, and pancreas.

❖ ❖

IT'S A FACT: Every cigarette smoked increases all the hazards for every age group. All the risks begin to decrease immediately when the smoker stops smoking.

The debate is over as to whether it is harmful to be on

the other end of the smoker's cigarette. It is. Passive smoking is now recognized as the third leading preventable cause of death—after active smoking and drinking. Nonsmokers living with smokers have a 30 percent (or higher, according to some studies) risk of death from heart attacks. And nonsmokers who live with smokers cannot be dismissed as the kinds of people who have heart attacks anyhow. The platelets of nonsmokers sitting for twenty minutes in a waiting room with smokers became stickier—a condition that leads to heart attacks.

In one study, 69 percent of nonsmokers developed eye irritation when among smokers; 29 percent had nasal symptoms; 32 percent had headaches; and 25 percent developed coughs. And these were the nonallergic nonsmokers. The percentages were much higher among those with allergies.

The nonsmoking majority is fighting back, and public places and work sites now often prohibit smoking. It is in the home that smokers most often find their victims—defenseless children.

DEATH BE NOT PROUD: Passive smoking is charged with annually causing 3,700 deaths from lung cancer and 37,000 deaths from heart disease. The total mortality rate from passive smoking is estimated at 53,000 per year—more than the number of deaths in car accidents.

| D A Y   3 0 | Many are the ex-smokers who have turned to cigarettes at

times of pressure. And just as many have been sorry afterward. When the heat is on, it's easy to forget your priorities, such as how much you care about not smoking. There you are, your mind agitated, when a devious thought comes to you: "I need a cigarette." And many months later, the only reason you may have to remember that day is that it was the day you started smoking again.

It's only the moment you have to get through, and the urge will pass. So be ready for it. Practice. Conjure up difficult situations in which you turn down cigarettes. There you are in the hotel bar late at night when your ex-wife walks in. You suffered for two years after she left. She looks better than ever. She's with her new husband. You're with a friend who smokes. DON'T REACH FOR HIS CIGARETTES. That sensation of a rib breaking in your chest will pass. You could be stuck with the cigarettes forever.

❖   ❖

"I suppose if I had to relive my life I ought to eschew the habit of smoking."

—WINSTON CHURCHILL

You've done it. A month without cigarettes. This is a time for

celebration—perhaps a long-distance call to someone who will appreciate this good news?

It's also time for one of your periodic countings of blessings. Think back to the state you were in when you smoked. Do you feel better now? Look better? Smell better? Sleep better? Do you get more done? Do you hold your head higher?

So maybe not. Maybe you're a nervous wreck. Maybe you chew your fingernails or scream at your children. Some people find themselves depressed at this point. If you smoked to avoid facing inner problems, the problems may have become much more apparent since you stopped smoking. But you still have something to be thankful for—at least you're on the road to recovery. You're not hiding in your private smoke shelter anymore. Possibly you could benefit from professional insight. Most medical plans offer short-term psychological help—and consider it particularly cost-effective in the case of people giving up smoking.

❖   ❖

"After I quit smoking, the cravings weren't too much, but I got seriously depressed. It was bad. Then one day a friend took me to a yoga class, and when I came home that first day I was on a high. I took eight yoga classes in the next eight days. Depression hasn't been a problem for me since I started yoga. I used to wonder what a natural high was, and now I know. Yoga works on many levels—on doubts and fears and cravings and fatigue. It's sort of a miracle. I feel lightness inside, and I'm smiling."
—DOUGLAS SANTOS, ex-smoker

```
 D A Y   3 2 
```
If you haven't been feeling well tuned in the head since you stopped smoking, there's plenty you can do about it. Regular exercise is one of the most beneficial. It will both calm you down and pep you up.

Regular conversation is important, too. Smokers very often have spent their years of smoking avoiding certain subjects. This isn't a problem if you aren't troubled or longing for cigarettes. But if you are, a confidante might help—therapist or friend. A good therapist will help you clear away some anxiety. But therapists cost money, sometimes too much. An understanding friend will listen to what's on your mind, although you may have to force the conversation beyond its usual limits. Men in particular often find it hard to expose their most profound worries.

There are plenty of self-help groups around. You might not think you're the type for them, but you'll find out in these groups that whatever your problems, you're not alone. There may be meetings of Nicotine Anonymous in your community—ex-smokers helping one another. You will almost certainly find other twelve-step programs, men's groups, and women's groups.

❖   ❖

"I could see that this sort of thing [quitting smoking] could be disastrous to a marriage. I have friends who just yelled at each other for weeks."

—JACQUETTA NISBET, *ex-smoker*

The infants and children of smoking parents are at high

risk for pulmonary problems, middle ear infections, complications of asthma, and heart disease. Their lungs show reduced airway size, and blood tests prove that they have higher cholesterol levels than the children of nonsmokers.

An Israeli study demonstrated that children whose mothers smoked more than a pack a day had three times the rate of hospitalizations for bronchitis and pneumonia as the children of nonsmokers. Cigarettes have long been suspected of contributing to Sudden Infant Death Syndrome (SIDS), and a Swedish study of 279,000 infants documented 2 to 3 times as many deaths from SIDS among the newborns of smokers.

The children of smokers grow up to have elevated rates of heart disease even if they don't smoke themselves. Unfortunately, the children of smokers are very likely to smoke themselves—twice as likely as the children of nonsmokers.

THE ODDS: *Children of smoking parents have a 17 percent higher rate of lymphocytic leukemia and a 6 percent higher rate of other cancers. One study found that a group of children who had developed cancer before the age of ten were 2.5 times more likely to have smoking mothers than children without cancer.*

D A Y 3 4

There are yet more reasons to be grateful that you are not a smoking parent. It's hard to interact with children when you're busy with cigarettes. When little ones climb into your lap, you have to worry about poking them with a lit cigarette. When you feel the need for a smoke, you are less alert to children's needs. Smoking parents are inclined to skip the Girl Scout camping trip because the thought of it makes them tired, and besides, they're not supposed to smoke in the woods.

If your children are themselves smoking now, your quitting may lead to their quitting—just as your smoking led to their smoking. Grown children who don't smoke are going to be much happier to have you in their homes than they used to be. And they certainly will look forward more to visiting you.

Your children are particularly lucky that they have gained a parent far more likely to be self-sufficient in old age. Most old smokers are in bad shape. Your future is much brighter than it was 34 days ago.

❖ ❖

FAMILY LOYALTY: In one study of men trying to quit smoking, the biggest determinant of relapse was having a father who had been unable to quit.

It is a popular refrain with many smokers that, statistics

notwithstanding, they themselves are in the pink of health. There is sometimes a grain of truth in this, and one can wish that such superb constitutions were unleashed to more rewarding pursuits than smoking. More often, the smoker is not as fit as he or she claims but has no sense of what good health is.

The ravages of smoking are cumulative. Every cigarette shortens a life, each one leaving behind a permanent deposit of tar in the throat and lungs. The tissue lining the lungs and the bronchial tree is directly exposed to inhaled smoke; most lung cancers get their start in the linings of the bronchial tree. You can feel fine today and die of cancer next year—or of any number of other diseases you would have been spared had you not smoked.

There's always some hundred-year-old turning up to declare that the secret of his long life was whiskey and cigarettes. So what? That's someone who has overcome one-in-a-million odds. Your chances are better of winning the lottery.

Caveat Emptor: Lucky Strikes was introduced in 1916 and promoted by famous opera singers. Tenor Giovanni Martinelli was later challenged about his claim in an ad that Luckies did not irritate his throat. "How could they?" he retorted. "I have never smoked."

| **D A Y   3 6** | Let's look at money. The economics of smoking are a

weighty subject, from any angle. First, there's the ever-rising price of cigarettes. In many states, a mere pack a day costs over $800 per year. (That could be almost three times as much if you lived in Canada.) But that's minor compared to the secondary costs of smoking.

Each smoker costs a medical insurance plan an extra $400 per year. Smokers get in 50 percent more car accidents than nonsmokers. They start fires. They wear down air-conditioning systems. Their clothes need frequent cleaning and their apartments and offices need repainting. For all these reasons, they are expensive to hire.

However, a Stanford economist conjectures that smokers are not, contrary to popular theory, a burden to society because they so frequently drop dead before consuming their share of Social Security and private pension benefits. Blessing that this may be to society, it's an average $20,000 loss to the smoker himself.

Any way you look at it, your standard of living has zoomed upward since you stopped smoking.

❖ ❖

"The tremendous sum spent for tobacco is nothing but a monument to man's folly. Smoking would be stupid enough if you obtained your cigars and cigarettes for nothing. To pay for them is idiotic."

—BRUNO LESSING, *quoted in*
Tobacco Under The Searchlight, *1925*

Chronic Obstructive Pulmonary
Disease (COPD) is a catchall

term applying to obstruction of the airways, which usually involves degrees of chronic bronchitis, chronic emphysema, and/or asthma. About 12 million Americans have COPD, which is the fifth leading cause of death. Smoking is the main cause.

Three-quarters of COPD sufferers have chronic bronchitis, suffering from long-term inflammation in the bronchial tubes (the two large windpipes going into the lungs). In chronic obstructive bronchitis, the tubes have become narrowed, usually because of smoking, and breathing is threatened. It's like a blockage in a car's gasoline line.

Any disease that threatens to cut off breath is extremely frightening, and people with COPD live with the knowledge that, unless something else kills them first, someday they will not be able to draw another breath. Modern medicine offers life-extending therapies, but no cure. The most important therapy is stopping smoking, which will slow the progress of the disease.

COPD usually starts early in a person's smoking career, although the main symptom, breathing difficulty, doesn't manifest itself for many years. A chronic cough, wheezing, recurrent respiratory infections, weakness, reduced libido, and weight loss are among the early symptoms. If the smoker quits smoking in the early stage, he or she may avoid becoming a COPD fatality. Those who quit smoking after diagnosis extend their life expectancies.

❖   ❖

"There's nothing fair about the choice of victims for COPD. Some people smoke two packs a day and never get it. Other people are light smokers, and they do."
— MICHAEL S. STULBARG, M.D., *pulmonary specialist*

| D A Y   3 8 | You may have found that you have a lot more time on your

hands since you quit smoking. Smokers rarely realize it, but smoking is a very time-consuming hobby. Just the mechanics keep a person busy: First there's the little pause when you stop whatever you're doing, get the cigarettes out of your pocket or pocketbook, find a match, light up, and situate the ashtray—give that about 30 seconds. Then there's the time spent hauling that cigarette up to your lips and dragging on it. Maybe seven seconds. Say you do that about thirteen times per cigarette. That's two minutes each, multiplied by however many cigarettes you smoke a day. Even a pack-a-dayer loses forty minutes a day. This doesn't even count the time spent buying cigarettes, emptying ashtrays, etc. If you added up all the time you've spent on cigarettes, you probably could have gotten a Ph.D.

❖ ❖

LIFE STORY: *A German, who died at age 75, left behind a diary. In it he kept a record of the number of cigars he had smoked in his lifetime. The total was 628,715. The diary closed with these words: "I have tried all things. I have seen many. I have accomplished nothing."*
—WILL H. BROWN, Tobacco Under the Searchlight, 1925

A smoker should worry about a heart attack as much as about

cancer. Smoking a pack a day more than doubles the risk for both heart disease and sudden cardiac arrest—risks that are much greater to begin with than for cancer.

Smoking screws up the coronary system in a number of ways. In the first place, nicotine raises blood pressure, which increases the heart's work load and need for oxygen. Meanwhile, the blood carries less oxygen, which has been displaced by carbon monoxide.

Cigarette smoking is a large factor in the development of arteriosclerosis—a narrowing of the blood vessels from a buildup of plaque (fatty deposits and other junk). The definitive word isn't out on how it happens, but the suspicion is that something about smoking damages the inner layer of the arteries. Plaque sticks to damaged walls, a process encouraged by the stickier platelets in smokers' blood. Blood clots can form at the damaged sites, blocking the artery altogether.

It's also well established that smoking raises the amount of LDL (the bad cholesterol) in the blood and lowers the level of HDL (the good cholesterol). These levels quickly improve when someone stops smoking.

❖ ❖

DEFINITION OF A CIGARETTE: "A fire at one end, a fool at the other, and a bit of tobacco in between."

—*ANON.*

| D A Y   4 0 | Have you ever noticed how boring smokers can be? A few words, a pause, a big drag on the cigarette. . . . "Let's see. Where was I now?" Smokers are not by any means boring types. It's just that a boring conversation isn't bothering them as much as it is you because they're busy with something else— smoking. Meanwhile, you, the nonsmoker, are stuck concentrating on the dialogue.

Chances are that you, too, were less sprightly in the conversation department when you smoked, dragging out lunches and dinners while you fondled your cigarettes. Some people remain fascinating despite their smoking habits, but most of us need to bring all our faculties to the art of not boring others stiff.

❖   ❖

"We see some of our friends use tobacco, and although they know and will acknowledge that it is a nasty, loathsome and pernicious custom, yet they continue the practice."
—CHARLES WILLSON PEALE (1741–1827)

You should now be enjoying the smell of fresh air, the aroma

of food, and if you're lucky enough to live somewhere green, the scents of nature. If you aren't so lucky, why not plan a jaunt to the country? If you have the money (which you have, saved by not smoking), this would be a good time to book into one of those agreeable bed-and-breakfast places. They nearly all hate smokers, and you would have hated them when you smoked.

But now it's a different story. Now you are the kind of person they can afford to have around their mahogany-inlaid tables. These are quiet, restful inns in which you awake to the scent of freshly ground coffee. Then you lounge the morning away and later go for an invigorating walk, inhaling the perfume of flowers and foliage—or of rain or snow, as the case may be.

❖ ❖

"Smoking certainly does blunt a man's sense of cleanliness. . . .
If smokers were to be judged by the places they have left—by
the smoking-car after a long day's use, by the dinner-
table at which they have sat late, by the bachelor's
quarters when the bachelor has gone downtown—they must
be rated very low in the scale of civilization."
　　　—JAMES PARTON,
　　　　Does It Pay To Smoke and Drink? *1868*

| D A Y 4 2 | The job-hunting smoker faces an uphill battle. The sad fact is

that few employers want to take on the larger health insurance cost of a smoker, much less the incidental extras. Dr. William Weis, a professor of business at Seattle University, estimates that a company pays an additional $4,611 per annum for a smoker, which includes $1,820 for the time spent smoking, $500 for property damage, $486 for the sickening of non-smokers, $220 for absenteeism, and a few other items. Smokers start fires and wear down air-conditioning systems; their offices need frequent repainting. Who needs it? Even in no-smoking offices, people may object to sitting near the smoker, who exudes a stale tobacco odor.

For an ex-smoker, dreams of greener fields are much more realistic. Now that you're one of them, the time may have come to move onward and upward.

❖ ❖

"I employ no person who smokes cigarettes."

—THOMAS EDISON

Various studies have noted that smokers are often sensitive, cre-

ative people. If you're desperate to smoke, you might conclude that, having made you sensitive and creative, the Lord intended you to smoke. Hardly. For one thing, most sensitive, creative people don't smoke. The ones who do are the ones who want to be less so. So if you're a sensitive, creative smoker, you're less sensitive and creative than you would be if you didn't smoke.

This brings us to the matter of the too sensitive person. Perhaps the joys and sorrows of life are too much for him or her. Cigarettes once stabilized the ricochets of emotion.

Yes, and a bad job they did. Surveys galore have shown smokers to be more neurotic, depressed, angry, and rebellious than nonsmokers. If anything, cigarettes arrest development. There are vastly more productive ways to control excessive sensibilities. For less than the price of a pack of cigarettes, you can give the White House a piece of your mind (202-456-1111).

❖ ❖

"It is very likely ... that Kant's books would not have been written in so strange and bad a language if he had not smoked so much."
—LEO TOLSTOY, **Why People Become Intoxicated, 1890**

| D A Y   4 4 | The National Cancer Institute offers a nifty information service number (800-4-CANCER), which you can call even if you don't have cancer. The friendly characters you'll reach offer counseling to quitters and will help you with suggestions for things to do this minute to avert a walk to the store for cigarettes. They can send you one of their "Smoking Packages" and even refer you to quit-smoking programs in your area. If there's anything you do want to know about cancer, they've got up-to-date information on diagnosis and treatment for any cancer you can name. You can call from 9:00 A.M. to 7:00 P.M. and speak in Spanish or English.

❖   ❖

EARLY GRAVES: Here's a partial list of famous people carried away prematurely by lung cancer: Edward R. Murrow, John Wayne, Gary Cooper, Chet Huntley, Lee Remick, Sarah Vaughan, Dick Powell, Yul Brynner, Walt Disney, Franchot Tone, Ed Sullivan, King George VI of England, Leonard Bernstein, Duke Ellington, Buster Keaton, Nat King Cole, Colleen Dewhurst, Boris Pasternak, Thomas Schippers, Eddie Kendricks, Elaine de Kooning, and Alan Jay Lerner. They all had one thing in common—smoking.

A smoker looking for romance carries a major liability. To put

it bluntly, the idea of kissing a smoker is not appetizing to a nonsmoker. "When I see a woman light up, she just goes off my screen," says Bob Kubik, an ex-smoker. So the smoker had best look for another smoker. But in a world in which it's already hard enough to meet someone compatible, the odds go way down when looking for a compatible smoker. Particularly if one is inclined toward educated types; smokers with college degrees make up under 16 percent of the population. Smokers had better lower their expectations and try their luck at seedy bars.

❖ ❖

"I am not ... what is called a ladies' man, having contracted an irrepressible habit of smoking after dinner, which has obliged me to give up a great deal of the dear creatures' society; nor can I go to country homes for the same reason."

—WILLIAM MAKEPEACE THACKERAY,
The Confessions of Fitz-Boodle, 1852

DAY 46

A former Winston Man, David Goerlitz, now devotes himself to urging youngsters not to smoke. In his days as Winston Man, he was paid $100,000 a year to look healthy and virile in Winston cigarette advertisements. But unlike most models in cigarette ads, he actually was a heavy smoker. Consequently, when posing on mountaintops, where the air was thin, he required an oxygen tank. In his mid-thirties, he had a stroke. However, he continued smoking until, when visiting his brother in a cancer ward, he met the victims of lung cancer.

Goerlitz now tells schoolchildren—the targets of much cigarette advertising—the truth about smoking. Seventy-five percent of all smokers start under the age of 14. "Kids are not thinking about death," says Goerlitz, which makes them susceptible to ads that show dashing people doing risky things. In looking back, Goerlitz now considers that, as Winston Man, he was "a high-priced accessory to murder."

❖ ❖

"We don't smoke the crap, we just sell it."
—CIGARETTE COMPANY EXECUTIVE,
as quoted by David Goerlitz, 1991

Iva Keefe smoked two packs a day for 30 years and landed

one day in the hospital with Chronic Obstructive Pulmonary Disease (COPD). "I'd had a cold and was short of breath but never imagined this. The tragedy of smoking is the attitude 'It won't happen to me.' Then when you do get sick, it's too late and you can never get well."

Mrs. Keefe has had three hospitalizations now, at one time spending 18 days in a coma. Her diagnosis of COPD includes degrees of bronchitis, emphysema, and asthma, for which she takes a variety of medicines. Prednisone, a steroid, is her mainstay, but prednisone has devastating side effects.

It was a blow for Mrs. Keefe to give up her rewarding career, but she finally admitted, "It just wasn't worth it. I covered five western states, and I couldn't carry my briefcase. I couldn't get the rental car. At meetings, I could hardly talk. My husband says I look a lot better since I retired, but I haven't yet figured out what to do with myself.

"I'm limited. I have oxygen at night, and when I walk I have to stop a lot. I can't climb stairs. There's a lot to manage with a disease like this. The Better Breathers Club, run by the American Lung Society, is very helpful."

❖   ❖

"If I had known as a girl what I know now, I never would have started. I can still remember the first cigarette I ever smoked; it made me dizzy. I don't know why I ever smoked another."

—IVA KEEFE, *ex-smoker*

D A Y   4 8

It's possible that on your way to Day 48, you've had a slip and smoked one or more cigarettes. As a matter of fact, this would not be unusual. Just don't look at your slip as evidence that you don't have the makings of a nonsmoker. Some people quit once and forever, but the majority of ex-smokers get there by the bumpier road. The average person goes through seven stops and starts before the permanent stop. Clearly, the trick to quitting is to keep trying.

If you do smoke, make it a learning experience. Notice the taste, smell, and effect of cigarettes. Having once tried to stop, you're not going to like yourself while smoking, so don't waste any time knocking off again. Every time you quit, you learn things that make you better at quitting. Eventually, you'll quit for good.

For those succeeding on the first go-round: Be thankful and don't entertain the thought that you have some more smokes coming to you. The longer quitting takes, the more painful it is. Far better to be done with cigarettes now and forever.

Today's Tip: If you do smoke again, collect the butts in a glass jar. Fill it half full of water and keep it around the house. Throw in any new butts you create.

Every time you outwit the desire to smoke, something happens to you. Like Ulysses, you conquer. A person smokes to escape; if instead of escaping you face up to reality and live with it, you become a stronger person.

You may not be an easier person to live with. Reality can be hard. After a mere 49 days, you may not be comfortable with it. Give it time. It could be years before you attain an easy state of mind. You may never hit total serenity. But at least you'll be alive, in mind and body, rather than drugged with nicotine and weak of lung and spirit.

❖ ❖

"My lady, what ordeals have we not endured! Here, waiting you had your grief, while my return dragged out—my hard adventures, pitting myself against the gods' will, and Zeus, who pinned me down far from home. But now our life resumes: we've come together to our longed-for bed."
   —HOMER, The Odyssey, *translated by Robert Fitzgerald*

| D A Y   5 0 | Time to review your exercise program. Do you have one? Is it adequate? Are you getting better at whatever you do? Does it fit nicely into your day and do you feel pleasantly relaxed afterward? If it's a good exercise program, it's one you enjoy enough not to skip without a good reason. If instead you feel a general dread of exercising, you ought to explore other kinds of exercise.

There are people who become exercise addicts, craving exercise excessively. This indeed can be a problem, rife with escapism, neglect of family, and even abuse of body. But at the moment—50 days from cigarettes—it's not likely to be as big a problem as smoking. Someday, maybe next year, you may need to worry about moderating your exercise mania.

❖ ❖

"I'd run for years with a friend, smoking or not. She was much faster than I was but would stay back with me. One day after I'd quit smoking for a few months we joined a 10K run that went over Capitol Hill, which had always been brutal for me. This time we started up the Hill and something came over me. I turned to Sue and said, 'I'll see you later,' and just left her in the dust. I couldn't believe it."

—*MARY G., ex-smoker*

Lung cancer was a very rare disease in the United States before the 1920s. Today it is the most common form of cancer and accounts for 25 percent of all cancer deaths. Not coincidentally, cigarette smoking did not become commonplace until the 20th century. The increase in lung cancer cases has closely followed the upward curve in cigarette smoking, allowing for a 20-year lag for the cancers to develop. A recent reduction in cases among white men reflects their drop in smoking rates since 1965. Lung cancer among women (who started to smoke heavily after World War II) is still increasing and now surpasses breast cancer as women's leading cause of cancer death.

Smokers are 20 times more likely to die from lung cancer than nonsmokers. The risk increases with the number of cigarettes smoked. As a quitter, your risk of lung cancer is now decreasing, but a recent study by the American Cancer Society showed that someone who smoked for 15 years or more will always have a higher risk for lung cancer than a never-smoker. However, the younger you are when you quit, the more the risk decreases, and even people who quit in their early sixties cut in half their risk of dying of lung cancer by age 75.

❖ ❖

"My father died of lung disease caused from smoking the family brands, Camel and Winston. . . . The hand that fed me is also the hand that has killed thousands more."
     —PATRICK REYNOLDS,
     Patrick Reynolds, Foundation for a Smokefree America

```
D A Y   5 2
```
There are very few smokers who answer "yes" when asked "If you could do it again, would you take up smoking?" And yet smokers continue to smoke, gripped by a frighteningly addictive drug.

Smoking is now decreasing in Europe and the United States, but it is increasing everywhere else. One of every five people in the future is expected to have a death hastened by tobacco—some of them nonsmokers suffering from the effects of sidestream smoke.

American tobacco companies foresee that their greatest profits lie overseas, and they are vigorously promoting cigarettes in Third World countries. The ministries of health of these countries preach against cigarettes, but the allure of cigarette tariffs to a poor government is great, and those who resisted have been heavily pressured by the United States to open their markets to American cigarettes.

❖   ❖

"For the past 100 years America has been the world's foremost exporter of public health ... now the U.S. trade representative wants to add a new chapter to that legacy ... a chapter entitled: America, the world's greatest exporter of lung cancer, heart disease, emphysema, and death."

—TED T. L. CHEN AND ALVIN E. WINDER,
American Journal of Public Health, *June 1990*

"People are tied to smoking as Gulliver was tied to the ground

by the Lilliputians: through hundreds of individual threads," writes David Krogh in *The Artificial Passion*. Any desire incorporates a degree of behavioral conditioning: Drinkers want to drink when the six o'clock news comes on, overeaters salivate on passing a bakery, and lovers grow limp when hearing "their" song. The problem that ex-smokers have is that they're conditioned to associate cigarettes with almost everything.

So the smoker thinks of smoking when he 1) gets up in the morning; 2) drinks coffee; 3) drives to work; 4) opens the mail; 5) goes to a meeting; 6) has another cup of coffee; 7) makes a phone call; and so on. None of these events seem complete without a cigarette. Any one of them can trigger the old longing, even if withdrawal from cigarettes took place quite long ago.

Changing the conditioning is only a matter of surviving without cigarettes long enough. Eventually, the sands of time fill in the holes left by cigarettes, and the whole idea of smoking in any circumstance becomes a surprising and distant memory.

Rx: When you want to smoke, hop in the shower. Few people associate showering with smoking.

| D A Y 5 4 |

Tobacco was unknown in Europe until the discovery of the New World. Columbus himself was probably the first to transport tobacco across the sea, and tobacco from America enriched the Spanish treasury as gold never did.

American Indians used tobacco more for religious than for medicinal purposes, but the myth spread that Indians employed tobacco as a panacea for all their ills. European doctors began enthusiastically prescribing oil of tobacco for a wide variety of ailments, probably killing many patients.

Smoking had become popular in Spain and Portugal by the early sixteenth century, but it was not until after 1586, when Sir Francis Drake brought quantities of Virginia tobacco home to England, that great numbers of Englishmen began to smoke. There was immediate opposition to the habit, but people went on smoking then for the same reason they do now: they quickly became addicted.

❖ ❖

"I have known Spaniards in this island of Hispaniola who were wont to take them [tobacco], and being reproved for it and told it was a vicious habit, they replied that it was not in their power to stop. I know not what pleasure or comfort they find in them."

—FERNANDO COLOMBO (1488–1539),
History of Don Fernando Colombo

For seriously depressed people, quitting smoking may be next to impossible.

Although most people become less depressed in time after quitting smoking, those who are clinically depressed may genuinely have derived some relief from the effect of nicotine on the brain.

According to Dr. Alexander Glassman, of the New York State Psychiatric Institute, stopping smoking for people with histories of depression can precipitate serious depressions. He suggests that antidepressants are likely to help such people succeed in giving up smoking.

If you fall into this category and at this point are suffering from depression, you should see a doctor. Depression is a terrible thing and should not be borne, but smoking is only a Band-Aid. Among the many available antidepressants, there is help for nearly everybody.

❖ ❖

FOR THE RECORD: *Among nonsmokers, 2.9 percent have suffered major depressions; among smokers, the figure is 6.6 percent.*

| D A Y   5 6 |

Rear Admiral Gerald Synhorst was 47 years old when he got the bad news. He'd just received a plum assignment in the Mediterranean, and people were calling him "Admiral Rickover's heir apparent." Three weeks earlier he'd passed his annual physical with flying colors, but on ship tours, he was having trouble keeping up. He returned to his doctor for a more thorough checkup. A few tests later, the doctor stamped his chart " UNFIT FOR ACTIVE DUTY."

He had serious chronic emphysema. That was the end of his navy, or any other, career. He gave up smoking and died eleven years later, in 1986.

Before he died, he wrote in an article for *The Saturday Evening Post:* "I thought I didn't have time to work on my addiction . . . I had a navy to run . . . I had a VIP complex.

"I had a marvelous life and career in the navy, but I could have had all that without the smoking, and it wouldn't have been cut short at age 47. I could have had all the enjoyment without the cigarettes. . . . Smokers know about naggers—their wives, their children, their mothers, their sisters, and their lovers. Listen to those who love you and pray to God for strength to fight the addiction."

❖ ❖

"The reason my dad and his neighbors weren't dying from lung cancer, heart disease, or emphysema was that [during the Depression] even roll-your-own cigarette tobacco was in short supply."

—REAR ADMIRAL GERALD SYNHORST,
The Saturday Evening Post, 1986

You've got eight weeks of non-smoking under your belt now.

As you put some distance between yourself and your last cigarette, it's important to keep alive the memory of the state you were in when you decided to stop smoking. Memory tends to soften pain and enhance pleasure. So instead of dwelling on the fleeting moments when the smoke hit your brain in the right spot, let's review the larger picture.

First, there was that raw throat. It was painful when you coughed, and you coughed pretty often. Your lips were dry and cracked. You got colds you couldn't shake. And sometimes you'd feel a sharp stab in your lungs, which you attributed to heartburn. Your wind wasn't good. Going upstairs you'd stop on the landing to catch your breath. Occasionally you felt faint for no reason, and you were just plain tired a lot. Sometimes your fingers felt numb, and you were often cold. You rarely thought to connect any of this with smoking, but now that you've stopped, the aches and coughs and dryness are gone. And so are the yellow stains on your fingers that you couldn't pretend came from anything but smoking.

❖ ❖

"I had a headache the whole time I smoked and didn't even know it."

—DIANE CLEAVER, *ex-smoker*

Successful quitters, whether going it alone or taking part in a quitting program, seem to be those who have turned some mental corner regarding cigarettes. With a fixed image of yourself as a nonsmoker, the quitting process becomes much easier. It's those who maintain doubt in their minds about their status who suffer the most and are likeliest to smoke again.

"I tried to quit the whole time I smoked," says Meryl Evens. "I stopped smoking when I was pregnant but then started again and was one of those awful mothers with a baby at the breast and a cigarette in her hand. And then one day when my daughter was three years old, I woke up in the middle of the night thinking that I might not even live to see her grow up. It was terrifying. And I knew I would never smoke again. Never. After that, quitting was easy and I haven't thought about smoking since."

❖　❖

LEGAL DEPARTMENT: In deciding child custody cases, courts have begun to downrate homes with smoking parents.

Unless you're entirely certain

that you've turned the corner and will never smoke again, there are probably situations you should stay out of. Stressful ones are at the top of the list, but, of course, not all stress is preventable. If you could avoid someone in your family getting sick, your house being foreclosed, or your unemployment running out, you probably would. But there are other risky setups under your control.

One man who'd spent thousands of dollars at residential stop-smoking programs finally succeeded in staying off cigarettes for two months. Then he accepted an invitation to visit chain-smoking friends at their villa in Turkey. It was a surprise to no one that when he returned home he was a smoker again.

Travel, while often delightful, is often stressful and has been the undoing of many well-intentioned quitters. It may be better to master not smoking at home before taking shaky avoidance skills on the road.

You may need to avoid your smoking friends. Rather than hurt their feelings, explain the reason to them. You'll be doing them a favor; there are doubtless others who don't like being around them and their cigarettes and don't tell them why. You may feel like a dope, but you'd be a bigger dope to end up with a cigarette in your mouth.

❖ ❖

"When I see people smoking now, they sort of don't exist as options for me, as people I need to be friends with."
—CAROL WHITMAN, ex-smoker

DAY 60

There is no shortage of expertise on how to quit smoking, but the experts ruefully admit that they know much less about how to prevent relapses. Consequently, the analysis of relapses is a hot subject of study. Saul Shiffman of the University of Pittsburgh has extensively examined those moments when ex-smokers grapple with—and sometimes succumb to—temptation. These relapse crises can be categorized (negative feelings, social situations, under the influence), but Shiffman has concluded that it is not the situations themselves that caused the relapses but a failure to enact coping mechanisms.

What's more, it doesn't much matter what coping mechanism is used. "A variety of specific cognitive and behavioral coping strategies were about equally effective," writes Shiffman. The important thing was for the ex-smoker to do or think *something*.

Interestingly, most of the relapse crises were not associated with withdrawal symptoms. Withdrawal is the part most people can handle. It's everything else in life that can undo your success. So keep your coping mechanisms sharp, whatever they are. What would you do or think right now if you were suddenly overcome with a craving for a cigarette?

❖ ❖

"The majority of those who achieve abstinence from tobacco . . . relapse within six months."

—SAUL SHIFFMAN, *University of Pittsburgh*

When people have eye trouble, it doesn't often occur to

them—or to their doctors—that their smoking habits could be to
blame. But smoking increases intraocular pressure and puts
smokers at greater risk of developing glaucoma. Cataracts
are three times more common in heavy smokers than in nonsmokers.

A serious eye problem called amblyopia is also associated
with smoking. Amblyopia produces a dimming of vision in the
central part of the visual field and is related to a vitamin B_{12} de-
ficiency. Smokers do not absorb B_{12} effectively and much more
commonly suffer from amblyopia than nonsmokers.

❖ ❖

*"Among the evils which afflict man we add another: a plant
whose smoke has darkened Europe. What can be worse than
to pollute the air and to turn the stomachs near one? . . .
Enough of this insane thing."*

—JEAN SCHOLASTIQUE PITTON,
On Writing the Natural History of Provence, 1672

```
  D A Y   6 2
```
Smokers themselves only inhale one-fiftieth of the carcinogens their cigarettes produce. The rest, along with all the other irritants from burning tobacco, pollute the surrounding air. Few nonsmokers have ever liked sharing the air with tobacco smoke, but the modern age until recently has been very tolerant of smokers. Now nonsmokers are winning ever-expanding rights based on the many definitive studies that show that cigarette smoke makes nonsmokers sick.

One solution, a nearly impossible one, is to ventilate rooms sufficiently to remove the pollutants. To reduce the carbon monoxide in a room with smokers to a nonirritating level (below 2.0 parts per million) requires five times as much ventilation as in a room with nonsmokers. And to protect people from the carcinogens from cigarettes would require turning over the air 250 times more than normal. That means 250 times the heating and 250 times the cooling—hardly an energy-efficient approach. Instead, it is only reasonable that smokers should practice their avocation in the outdoors.

SORRY FACT: Exposure to tobacco in the U.S.A. is so universal that in a major federal study the first 800 people tested showed signs of nicotine in their bodies—both smokers and nonsmokers.

The matter of smokers' rights

has been considerably fanned by the tobacco companies but has failed to gather a large following. The right to smoke is a curious right, insofar as no inherent good has been found in smoking and the right to kill oneself has been consistently denied. Nonetheless, over two dozen states—most predominantly tobacco states—have passed laws decreeing a legal right to smoke. Tobacco lobbyists wield great power in state legislatures.

West Virginia, where tobacco is the leading crop, has legislated rights only for smokers; nonsmokers have none. The legislators claim that antismoking legislation has little public support. This is false, despite the fact that West Virginia has one of the highest smoking rates in the country. A poll found that three-quarters of West Virginians, many of them smokers, favor smoking restrictions.

FOR THE RECORD: A person smoking a pack a day puts as many mutagenic substances into the air as someone driving twenty-two miles in a car with a catalytic converter.

```
┌─────────────────────┐   Patience is not a quality you
│   D A Y   6 4       │   find much among smokers. Pa-
└─────────────────────┘
```
tient people aren't likely to take up smoking in the first place
because they don't require something to fill up the crevices in
their days. And those who start smoking at a young age don't
develop patience because their drug is readily at hand.

By this time, your nervous system should be in better shape
and your equilibrium improved. But patience, that great virtue,
is something else, and your store of it may still be pretty small.
You've had very little practice at waiting. You smoked instead.
And the brain that's full of smoke hasn't got space for inner
calm. As a nonsmoker, you've got a shot at building up some
patience. You may never be Job, but those who are drug-free
often discover that creeping along with age and wisdom
comes patience.

❖   ❖

"When I smoked, I was a 'pulsive' person: impulsive,
compulsive, repulsive."

—PATTY A., *ex-smoker*

If quitters have a patron saint, it is surely Saint Rose of Lima,

who was canonized in 1671. One of Saint Rose's miracles was the conversion of a confirmed smoker into a nonsmoker. Her subject was a monk who had smoked for thirty years and saw nothing wrong in it. All the supplications of his friends, his superiors in the monastery, and those of his doctor had fallen on deaf ears.

Saint Rose spoke with him and then prayed for him. Five days later he became nauseated with tobacco, stopped smoking forever, and recuperated from a respiratory ailment.

PRAYER: *Dear Saint Rose, may your spirit enter me and relieve me of my craving for tobacco. May the thought of tobacco fill me with disgust and may I rejoice in breathing God's clean air instead. Let me be grateful for the marvelous workings of my pulmonary system, which was not designed to be laced with smoke. May I recover from the damage I have done to my body through smoking, and may my lungs be pink when I go out of the world, as they were when I came into it.*

DAY 66

One of the attractions of smoking is the little high you might have gotten from it. "Toning" is a surprisingly effective way to get a nice natural high. It's very simple: stand or sit in an erect posture. Close your eyes and take a deep breath. Let out the breath slowly while singing a single note. Do it on a vowel sound—"ah" and "oh" are good places to start. When you're out of breath, take another big breath and let your noise out again. Keep this up for five or ten minutes.

You can experiment with different sounds and tones, low notes and high ones. If you want to, you can keep at it for twenty minutes, but even a short session produces a groovy feeling. Toning is a wonderful way to clear the mind, and a nice transition from one activity to another. And if you want to smoke now, you won't after your toning session.

"The only time I ever took a deep breath used to be when I was dragging on a cigarette. I didn't realize I could take a big calming deep breath without a cigarette."

—SALLY T., ex-smoker

Cigarette smoke is composed of gases and tiny particles of

unburned tobacco. The tiny particles are the tar, which is what ruins the lungs. Droplets of nicotine, the addictive component, float along in the tar. The main gases are nitrogen, oxygen, and carbon monoxide, which are mixed with 400 to 500 other gases, many deadly, such as hydrogen cyanide, benzene, toluene, and formaldehyde.

Nicotine breaks down quickly in the body. About half of it clears out of the bloodstream within 15 to 30 minutes, which accounts for the average smoking cycle. Tolerance to nicotine builds up rapidly so that as the day wears on, a smoker gets less and less stimulation or soothing from cigarettes and is reduced to lighting cigarettes to stave off withdrawal pangs.

Additives make the modern cigarette what it is; there are humectants, casing agents, and flavorings. In addition, pesticides, fertilizers, and metals are picked up from the soil. Even a few radioactive elements, such as postassium-40, lead-210, and radium-226, work their ways in.

❖ ❖

TOBACCO POWER: How do cigarettes get by the Food and Drug Administration? You might well ask. In exchange for support from the tobacco states for the Food and Drug Act of 1906, tobacco was removed from classification as a drug. Cigarette ingredients are subject to only the most minimal restrictions.

D A Y   6 8

A lot of people treasure cigarettes as a funny little punctuation system in their lives.

"A soon as I finish the dishes, I'll have a cigarette." "I've eaten my dinner so now I can smoke." "I made that phone call so now I'll have a cig." "Now that I've packed the kids off to school, I can sit down and smoke." "I'll have a cigarette, then I'll plant the next row."

The idea of carrying on without rewards for all one's noble efforts can be an unspeakable thought. But what do such people imagine keeps nonsmokers going? The unlikely truth is that if you aren't a nicotine addict, the activity—or getting it done—is its own reward. Besides, doing the things you have to do isn't as hard when you don't smoke. When you have a sense of well-being, the events of your day flow more pleasantly together. If you need to, you can insert other parentheses and exclamation points into your day: a look at the newspaper, a cup of tea, a moment at the piano, a snack, a chat. You will discover in time, if you haven't already, how little you need cigarettes.

❖   ❖

"Tobacco is the worst curse of modern civilization."
—JOHN RUSKIN (1819–1900)

As Virginia farmers, Thomas Jefferson and George Washington

ton were inevitably tobacco growers. Both, however, had a low regard for tobacco. They knew it was a crop exhausting to the soil and saw that farmers became so consumed by it that they failed to raise adequate food. Washington diversified his crops as much as possible and after 1773 planted only a negligible amount of tobacco.

In his 1868 Book, *Does It Pay to Smoke and Drink?* James Parton wrote of Thomas Jefferson: "In America, the best gentleman and most variously learned and accomplished man we have had . . . was Thomas Jefferson, Democrat, of Virginia. He was versed in six languages, he danced, rode, and hunted as well as George Washington; he played the violin well, wrote admirably, farmed skilfully, and was a most generous, affectionate, humane and great-souled being. It was [his] destiny to raise tobacco and live by tobacco all his life. But he knew too much to use it himself."

❖ ❖

"[Tobacco] is a culture productive of infinite wretchedness."
—THOMAS JEFFERSON (1743–1826)

```
D A Y   7 0
```
Smoking reduces the average weight of infants born to smoking mothers by a tenth, a fact established by studies worldwide. An underweight baby is much more likely to be a sickly baby, and these low birthweight babies are at higher risk of developing serious illnesses. In a United States study, babies of smoking mothers were twice as likely to be premature. An Italian study showed smokers miscarrying 250 percent more than nonsmokers.

The fetus of a smoking mother is receiving an undersupply of oxygen and an oversupply of carbon monoxide. The toxic chemicals in tobacco, just one of which is radioactive polonium, may all interfere with fetal development. The fetus receives these toxins directly through the mother's blood, whether the mother smokes, chews, or takes snuff. However, if the mother stops smoking before the fourth month of pregnancy, the risks of stillbirth and low birthweight return to normal.

Best Buy: For each $1 spent on smoking-cessation programs for pregnant women, $6 would be saved, according to an article published in 1991 in the American Journal of Preventive Medicine. *The calculation was that if the programs cost $30 per participant, and 15 percent quit smoking, enough babies would be spared treatment in neonatal intensive care to provide the savings.*

Your physical addiction to cig- | **D A Y   7 1** |
arettes is theoretically gone,
but statistically speaking you're still in danger of smoking. Having practiced smoking long and steadily, you are unlikely to be totally free of the habit so soon, and many ex-smokers are still plagued by increased hunger and cigarette cravings six months after quitting.

When you smoked, you used cigarettes to relax, and so you may still react to stress with an urge to smoke. Keep reminding yourself that smoking would make your stress worse, not better.

Leo Tolstoy once wrote that you cannot go around the brain, you can only go through it. If something is bothering you, and so you smoke, you are attempting to go around the brain. The thing that troubles you will linger unresolved. If you face up to it and let the anxiety wash through your brain, it will dissipate and float away. The mind of a smoker is apt to be clogged with uncomfortable thoughts, which the smoker keeps at bay by puffing and puffing and puffing.

❖ ❖

"I used to light a cigarette when I 'needed to think,' but what I really wanted was not *to think."*

—Don B., *ex-smoker*

DAY 72

The rewards for older people who quit smoking are just as great as for those in the prime of youth. Dorothy Andrews and Ruby Morris, life companions, had about a century of smoking between them. Along with a number of failed attempts to quit.

Two and a half years ago, Ruby heard Dorothy tell someone that she'd like to quit. "Then let's both quit," said Ruby. Neither have smoked since that moment. It was a project done together, and both say the other's support made all the difference. Mock fights ended in laughter. "As I was no longer medicating myself, I was shooting off my mouth more," Ruby says. "I think I've become a little more open and honest."

"I'm much more energetic," says Dorothy, who is now 74. "The nagging cough is gone, and I can climb the dunes without collapsing.

"I never thought about my health," says Ruby. "It was the guilt that goes with being a smoker that I hated. And waking up in the morning, thinking 'Here we go again, another day of chain-smoking.' But my health has improved. My breathing is much better. In a way, I think it's easier to stop when you're older. You've gotten used to giving up things; you know that you get other things in their place. And you know you're damn lucky to be alive."

❖ ❖

"Quitting from day to day, you feel almost as if you're under orders—your own—and you can suffer a lot but you can't give in."

—RUBY MORRIS, ex-smoker

Most smokers don't realize the
extent to which smoking rules

their lives and will often make their relationship to cigarettes sound far more casual than it is. Addictions make people dishonest—with themselves and with others. The smokers *must* smoke. Such a person may think he or she enjoys any number of things, but those other things are optional, unlike smoking, and they become secondary to smoking.

For instance, a smoker may profess to have adored every moment of *Aida* when, in fact, while Pavarotti was melting other hearts, she was contemplating the best means of persuading her date—without seeming like a madwoman—that despite a blizzard it would be nice to step outside during the intermission. Smokers may not really take great pleasure in anything outside of smoking. The cigarette is not (as they like to think) the cherry on top of the cake but the cake itself. One of the beauties of not smoking is that you get to develop a genuine and honest pleasure in the other events of life.

❖ ❖

Dying To Smoke: During World War II, some prisoners of war traded their food rations for cigarettes and starved.

| D A Y 7 4 | When hearing of someone di-agnosed with lung cancer, the

first question is often "Did she/he smoke?" Smoking doesn't come so quickly to mind when hearing of someone who has had a stroke, but it reasonably could. Although a great many nonsmokers suffer strokes, the risks rise dramatically for smokers—especially in the younger age groups.

The surgeon general rates the overall risk of stroke among smokers as two to four times that of nonsmokers. The risks are even higher for certain kinds of strokes, such as subarachnoid hemorrhages. In a study of nurses, those who smoked only 1 to 14 cigarettes a day had four times as many subarachnoid hemorrhages as nonsmokers. At 25 cigarettes a day, the risk was ten times as great.

Studies of identical twins, one smoking and one not, have shown much more arteriosclerosis in the carotid arteries (which supply blood to the head) among the smokers. In fact, pack years (number of packs per day times number of years smoked) are a greater predictor of carotid arteriosclerosis than any other factor, including hypertension and cholesterol levels.

THE ODDS: *A 1989 study of strokes concluded that the increase in risk among smokers was 1.5 for each ten cigarettes smoked daily. After quitting, the decrease in risk is rapid and steady, no matter how much one smoked.*

Modern life can provoke the
sense of being in a vise. This

comes when one has too much to do and not much enthusiasm
for any of it. At this point, the drinker goes on a bender, and
the smoker lights up. The cigarette may seem like the one flight
of fancy, the one bit of self-indulgence, in a life of drudgery.

So what do you do once sanity has deprived you of cigarettes? No life should be without sunshine. It may help to Just
Say No. "Kids," you say, "there will be no dinner tonight."
Whereupon you take the book you've been wanting to read
for a year and go to bed.

If you are the often-overwhelmed type, chances are that
you're a perfectionist. Which means that you never feel you've
done enough and that life tends to be a burden. Actually, it
doesn't have to be. Your first step is to find out what makes you
happy—starting for just a few minutes a day—and do it.

❖   ❖

*"If a woman has become accustomed to using cigarettes
as a means of coping with her stress and frustration, she
must find other outlets for her pent-up emotions before
she can successfully stop. Before she begins a smoking-
cessation program, she must deal with the feelings that are
driving her to light up. Often, counseling can be useful
to help these women develop coping skills that will
decrease their dependence on cigarettes."*
                    —MARIANNE J. LEGATO, M.D., AND CAROL COLMAN,
                    The Female Heart, 1991

| D A Y 7 6 | The effect of smoking on a man's sex life is likely to be

quite the opposite of what cigarette ads would have you believe. One study showed that men who smoke suffer a sharp decline in sexual activity between the ages of 25 and 40; men who don't smoke show a very slight decline. Smokers also have lower sperm counts and lower sperm mortality.

A study at Boston University of over 1,000 men with erection problems discovered that 70 percent of them were smokers. Smoking causes narrowing in the penile arteries, a reduction found to be proportional to the number of cigarettes smoked. Men who quit smoking often testify to greatly improved sex lives.

It should be recognized, of course, that a strong sex drive is not convenient to all men in all places. Some smoking men may smoke, consciously or not, to squelch desire. It can only be said that smoking is not a practical solution, any more than suicide could be recommended as a cure for a headache.

❖ ❖

"The penis is an organ that depends on inflow and outflow of blood. Much as if you were to tie a knot in an airhose, cigarettes impede the ability to achieve an adequate erection."

—DR. IRWIN GOLDSTEIN, *urologist*

Women have plenty of reasons
of their own to shun tobacco.

Women smokers are three times more likely than nonsmokers to
be infertile, with the heaviest smokers the most infertile. Warnings on cigarette packs remind us that smoking is hazardous to
the fetus.

Less well known is the fact that smoking women have lower
levels of prolactin (a hormone that stimulates the production of
milk) and so produce less milk and stop breast-feeding much
earlier than nonsmokers. A smoker's milk also has a lower fat
content and thus is less nutritional than a nonsmoker's milk.

Women who smoke reach menopause one and three-
quarters years sooner than nonsmokers. Following menopause,
the smokers are more prone to osteoporosis. In a Boston study,
postmenopausal smokers lost 1 percent of their bone mass
yearly while the nonsmokers lost virtually none. Both groups
took calcium, which smokers seem to have trouble absorbing.
On top of that, smokers have high rates of cervical cancer.

❖ ❖

*PANTY HOSES: Women who smoke suffer 3.5 times as much
stress incontinence as nonsmokers. It usually ceases as soon
as they stop smoking.*

Many writers have claimed that without tobacco they would be unable to function. This delusion has taken great numbers of them to the grave. Those who quit smoking have discovered how wrong they were and often have gone on to do their best work.

Jacob Riis (author of *How the Other Half Lives*) suffered from angina but smoked anyhow, in the belief that without tobacco he would lose his inspiration. Pain finally overcame him, and he quit. He later reported that he had been deceived—without tobacco his imagination was greatly improved.

Tolstoy felt that the nonsmoking writer wrote less, but better.

❖ ❖

"People generally say, and I used to say, that smoking contributes to mental work. This is unquestionably so, if one considers the amount of mental work. A smoker, who therefore has ceased to value strictly or to weigh his thoughts, imagines that a mass of ideas has suddenly come to him. But this does not mean at all that he has acquired a mass of thoughts, but only that he has lost control over his thoughts ... there will be more work, but its quality is lowered."

—LEO TOLSTOY, Why People Become Intoxicated, 1890

Fatigue is a great danger to the recent ex-smoker, which

you still are. When overtired, one lacks will and succumbs to old habits. So build ample rest time into your schedule. If you've got to choose between getting enough sleep and going out to the races, get enough sleep. Even if you're hyperactive and don't like resting, rest. This nation is full of people who keep going on coffee, cigarettes, and mental energy; they don't even realize how tired they are. The surprise is how pleasant it feels to be thoroughly rested. It's a goal worth striving for, and once you're revivified, the idea of cigarettes is less appealing.

❖   ❖

"One night recently I hardly got any sleep; the next day, my bones ached and it took a big effort just to walk up the hill going home. I recognized the weariness as the way I used to feel all the time when I smoked."

—KEN D., *ex-smoker*

A substantial number of perfectly normal drinkers have given up drinking in the course of giving up smoking. Some of them returned to the cocktail hour once they felt firmly established as nonsmokers. Others decided that a life without drink was a better life anyhow.

Bill Barton smoked from the ages of 18 to 58, when he became acutely troubled at exposing his baby granddaughter to smoke. He started smoking only in his den. She grew a little older and toddled down to the den after him. The only solution seemed to be to stop smoking. He'd already switched from cigarettes to a pipe, but as a pipe inhaler, he knew he hadn't helped his health. What's more, the pipe had made him no less of an addict: he played tennis with the pipe in hand.

Once committed to quitting, he foresaw one major pitfall: the evening cocktail. The smoke and the cocktail had been bound together into so pleasant a package that he couldn't picture one without the other. Barton is not a man to falter at tough choices. The evening cocktail would have to go.

In September 1985, the cocktail went. In October 1985, he bid tobacco good-bye permanently. Nicotine gum helped along the way. Drink didn't reenter Bill's life until the following June. The cocktail ritual is once again included in his day, but tobacco is not.

❖   ❖

It's A Fact: A few drops of distilled nicotine can kill a person.

There are people who will say,
"I can't talk on the telephone

without a cigarette," as if this were the ultimate excuse to smoke. They seem not to have noticed that the mass of humanity manages talking without smoking. Some of the latter also used to feel that God gave them two hands so that one hand could hold the telephone receiver and the other grip a cigarette. But today their conversations are rich and fulfilling, and they can hardly imagine what they wanted an ashtray for. There is no such person as one who can't talk on the phone without a cigarette.

But if you're one who still gets a hankering to smoke when the phone rings, try keeping some worry beads or a sheet of doodle paper or the therapeutic Chinese Iron Balls (available from Hammacher Schlemmer—800-543-3366) by the telephone. A portable phone is a godsend to nervous talkers because they can roam, weed the lawn, and talk simultaneously. And don't extend your conversations. You could end up saving time as well as lowering your phone bill.

❖ ❖

THE ODDS: *Various studies show smokers to have 8 to 14 times the risk for cancer of the larynx as nonsmokers—a sad end to many telephone conversations.*

Nora F. Crow, an English professor, stood staunchly behind her three-pack-a-day habit as long as she could. "I felt smoking made a political statement against the repressive tactics of people who were antismoking and politically correct. I rebelled against the constant onslaught of people frowning at me in restaurants, feigning allergies, and so on. I felt smoking was a way of opposing the fascism of antismokers."

She had other reasons for smoking, too. She'd quit once for 24 hours and all the joy and meaning of life had flooded away. Hearing ex-smokers mourn their cigarettes convinced her that a life without smoking would be forever a life without joy. Smoking was a constant friend. "I was so hardened a smoker that I even tried smoking in the shower using the soapdish as an ashtray."

At last, events overwhelmed even Crow's smoking. Her laryngitis wouldn't go away. She had two miscarriages and then bore a daughter, who, while normal, was a low birthweight baby. During her recent divorce, her husband brought Crow's smoking into the custody case. She started having stress incontinence. Finally, Crow chose the birthday of her father, who had died of emphysema, to go on the nicotine patch. Quitting was a belated present to him, and to her daughter, who had grown old enough to criticize her mother's smoking.

To her surprise, quitting wasn't as bad as she had expected. Her energy level soon shot up. And joy and meaning in life, she discovered, were not related to smoking.

❖   ❖

"Smoking is wasting your energy."
—NORA CROW'S DAUGHTER, *age six*

A strong association has been
shown between smoking and

cancer of the cervix. Two fairly recent studies found smokers
suffering 350 percent more cervical cancer than nonsmokers.
There is some controversy as to whether smoking actually
causes cancer of the cervics or whether smokers are more apt
to get sexual diseases that may cause cervical cancer. However, several studies have adjusted for the sex factor and still
found smokers at high risk. Furthermore, the risk goes down for
former smokers (and fairly rapidly, according to a large study
by the National Cancer Institute), which suggests that smoking
itself is a causal agent.

The association is unsurprising; compounds of tobacco
smoke can be found in the cervical mucus of smokers. These
compounds display mutagenic activity and can lower cancer
immunity in cervical tissues. In most studies, the risk of cervical
cancer for a former smoker averages out to about half that of
a current smoker.

❖ ❖

*"Review of the evidence on cervical cancer and cigarette
smoking cessation indicates that there is a consistently observed
association between cervical cancer risk and cigarette
smoking."*

—*The Health Benefits of Smoking Cessation,"*
The Surgeon General's Report, *1990*

The weight factor drives some quitters right back to smoking, defeated on two fronts. For normal people, a small weight gain should be nothing to worry about, but for Americans it's a critical matter. It's not a myth that quitters gain weight—70 percent do. But the chance of gaining an astronomical amount is low. Only 20 percent of quitters in one study gained 10 pounds or more, and only 3.4 percent gained over 20 pounds. The average gain is 4.6 pounds.

However, there's a lot of variation in what happens to smokers when they quit. Some lose weight. Many develop a taste for sweets. But others don't change their eating habits and still put on a few pounds. It seems that smoking can raise the resting energy expenditure (REE), making smokers burn more calories while doing nothing. If you are one whose REE appears to have gone down, you should now have more energy to spare for other things. Watching television may be too fattening for you, and it's time to take up more energetic endeavours. A short daily walk will compensate for the difference in REE.

❖   ❖

"I gained 30 pounds after I stopped smoking, and it took me five years to lose it. I was miserable, hated being fat, and looked awful, but now I'm a thin, nonsmoking vegetarian."

—TERRY W., *ex-smoker*

A lower resting energy expenditure (REE) is not the only reason ex-smokers seem to put on weight. The other is that they're eating more. If you weren't overweight before quitting and your body is only establishing a slightly higher setpoint, it's best to just accommodate your new three to five pounds. If you've gained serious amounts of weight, your thoughts may have turned to dieting. But dieting, from all evidence, only succeeds in making people both fat and hungry.

A more promising solution is diet improvement. The average American diet, heavy on fats and sugars, is a poor one. Loading up on fruits and vegetables instead is not only healthy and slenderizing but cuts the risk for many cancers in half. While a vegetarian diet is a drastic change for most people, giving up smoking is drastic, too. Having gone that far, you might as well do whatever's necessary to feel terrific.

❖   ❖

"When you make moderate changes ... you feel deprived because you can't eat or do everything you want, but the changes aren't enough to make you feel significantly better. But when you make comprehensive changes, you feel so much better so quickly that the choices become much clearer."
—DR. DEAN ORNISH, *author of* Dr. Dean Ornish's Program for Reversing Heart Disease *and* Eat More, Weigh Less

D A Y 8 6

One rationale smokers occasionally trot out is "We're all going to die anyhow and if a smoking disease doesn't get me, something else will." The rebuttal is obviously that if you smoke, the Grim Reaper comes around sooner. But at least you might hope, being dead, you'll be spending less money on medical care than someone who hangs around for many more years of doctors' visits and then sickens and dies.

But no. Even in their shorter lives, smokers use up more medical care than nonsmokers. The average extra cost per smoker is $6,300; the heavier the smoking, the higher the price. When you translate the money into the suffering, it makes a sad picture—a shortened life, with much debilitation from chronic disease, and all that nasty medical treatment. The nonsmoker is much more apt to live out his or her life span, then cheat the doctors by making a hasty departure.

❖   ❖

"Every day 3,000 children pick up their first cigarette because advertising says it's cool—smoke and you'll be popular. But we all know the truth. Smoking hurts people, smoking is a filthy habit, and smoking kills people."
—Dr. John L. Clowe, *president of the American Medical Association, 1992*

In the twentieth century, the United States has had a smok-

ing epidemic, which is now beginning to diminish, although mortality from smoking diseases remains high. The surgeon general's 1992 report predicted that less developed countries, without concerted resistance can look forward to following the same script: "gradual adoption of the smoking habit, long-term entrenchment of tobacco use, and a major loss of human life."

Following a rise in the GNP and intensified marketing by American tobacco companies, smoking greatly increased in Latin America during the 1960s and 1970s. The smoking rate fell during the recession of the 1980s, and the number of smoking deaths is still far lower in Latin America than in the United States, but smoking is increasing among young people and women, particularly among the affluent.

Tobacco companies are also chasing Eastern European markets, where "latent demand" is much greater than current consumption. Western cigarettes are madly popular and general ignorance prevails about the health effects of smoking. By the end of 1992, Philip Morris had bought its way into four Eastern European countries and was negotiating for others. The profit potential is huge. Philip Morris predicts that the Russians alone could consume 280 billion cigarettes a year—twice as many as they presently smoke.

❖ ❖

"In the tobacco industry ... the traditional elements of successful entrepreneurial activity ... are ultimately inimical to the public health."
—*ANTONIA NOVELLO, M.D., U.S. Surgeon General, 1990*

Manufactured cigarettes have been widely available for only a little over a hundred years. Before that, cigarettes were rolled by hand, and most people preferred pipes and cigars. When James Bonsack announced the invention of his cigarette-manufacturing machine in 1881, few tobacco companies saw a need for it.

James Duke, however, read the future and signed a contract with Bonsack. Soon, the Bonsack machine was producing 200 Duke of Durhams a minute, and Duke was able to cut prices in half—to five cents for a pack of ten cigarettes. By 1895, Americans were smoking almost 4 billion cigarettes a year.

With the proliferation of cigarettes, the antismoking movement took new fire. Nearly every state passed anticigarette legislation; New Hampshire banned cigarettes totally. Cigarette sales declined after 1896 for three years, but in 1902 began an upward climb. The smoking prohibitions were never much enforced and most were repealed by World War I. Advertising campaigns succeeded in making smoking fashionable for women. Cigarette consumption continued to rise until 1964—the year in which 50 percent of American men and 31 percent of American women smoked.

❖ ❖

"Cigarettes benefit from that almost perverse quality of human nature that makes what is despised and outlawed by some people absolutely irresistible to others."

—GORDON L. DILLOW, **American Heritage,**
February–March 1981

Jacquetta and Nori Nisbet are a couple who exemplify Try,

Try and Try Again. Says Mrs. Nisbet: "He smoked two packs a day and I smoked one, and we'd gone on that way for about forty years. We're lucky we're still alive."

The Nisbets first tried to quit by themselves and then tried one program after another. "We met wonderful people and did a lot of bonding, but went on smoking," Mrs. Nisbet says. "Finally, we found a program at Kaiser Hospital that gave us the sustained preparation that we needed to carry us through the hard moments.

"How do I feel now compared to when I smoked? There's no comparison. Wind, circulation, and endurance are dramatically better for both of us. My allergies went away; I suppose they were basically allergies to cigarettes. My voice has improved and I can sing again."

❖ ❖

*"It's during the breaks when I'm giving workshops that
I most want a cigarette. Then I remind myself that I suffered
far more when I smoked and had to endure three-hour
sessions without a cigarette than I do at those moments
in between."*

—JACQUETTA NISBET, *weaver, ex-smoker*

| D A Y   9 0 | On the whole, people who quit smoking can expect an improvement in mood. Numerous studies have shown quitters improving their scores on measures of anger, tension, fatigue, confusion, anxiety, and depression. The changes usually come slowly so it's not surprising if you're not feeling them yet. Here on Day 90, you've left most of your physical withdrawal symptoms well behind you, but many of the rewards of not smoking are still ahead of you.

One study of ex-smokers with a mean abstinence of two years found them to have significantly reduced anxiety and lower heart rates in response to simulated stressful situations. Another study compared 525 long-term former smokers of at least a year's abstinence with current smokers on the HAMES General Well-Being Index. The quitters scored significantly better than the smokers. A group of recent quitters—of less than a year—did not outshine the smokers. But other studies have shown notable improvements in "total mood disturbance" for quitters after six months, with those who had smoked the most getting the most improvement.

❖   ❖

"I don't feel a whole lot better physically since I quit smoking, but I do emotionally."

—CAROL WHITMAN, *ex-smoker*

Peripheral vascular disease is a condition commonly suffered

by smokers. In this disease, the vessels carrying blood to the leg and arm muscles become narrowed. Consequently, circulation is bad, and if a blood clot appears in these vessels, the end result can be the amputation of an arm or a leg. Ex-smokers are more apt to benefit from corrective surgery than smokers. Diabetics are at particular risk for peripheral vascular disease, and if they smoke, their risk sharply increases.

"In the classic case," says Dr. Arthur Chesterfield-Owens, "there's a fellow from whom you've lopped off one leg still addicted to smoking. In about two years, you lop off the other."

Many smokers merely endure sore feet, a result of bad circulation. Podiatrists should inquire about smoking habits.

❖   ❖

Smoker: "I must confess, smoking is the only pleasure I have in life. And therefore, I am not in favour of robbing any man of his tobacco, for I contend that the poorest wretch who ever trod the earth ought to be allowed to smoke if he so desires."

Fumigator: "Stop, stop! Have you never thought that tobacco is the greater robber, for does it not rob men of their health, sense and free will?"
    —*A. A. WILLIAMS,* A Smoker's Pilgrim's Progress, *1922*

D A Y 9 2

Ralph Scott, who smoked two to three packs a day for 35 years, claims he had no withdrawal symptoms after he quit. He took the pledge while lying on a gurney in a hospital emergency room, where he arrived following a probable heart attack.

"Fear is a great motivator," he said. "I think it reconstituted my body chemistry all at once. I no longer required nicotine." Tests later proved that Ralph's heart was sound; the attack had been an anxiety attack. (Anxiety attacks are not uncommon in smokers.)

Doctors recommended that Ralph also give up coffee, which he had drunk in abundance. He followed orders on this point, too, which may have eased his conversion into a nonsmoker. Smokers clear caffeine out of their systems much more quickly than nonsmokers, and some ex-smokers' withdrawal symptoms may actually result from excessive caffeine.

❖ ❖

"A case study by Sachs and Benowitz (1989) . . . found that symptoms of an apparent nicotine withdrawal syndrome (insomnia, increased weight, increased anxiety, and possibly restlessness) may have been partially the result of acute increases in plasma caffeine levels resulting from the diminished rate of caffeine metabolism."
—U.S. Department of Health and Human Services,
Drug Abuse and Drug Abuse Research, 1991

This is a day when you can afford a sigh of relief. You've

lasted three months without a cigarette and, statistically speaking, your chances of remaining a nonsmoker are good. Need-
less to say, that doesn't mean you can take not smoking for
granted. It certainly doesn't mean that you can afford to smoke
a single cigarette, thinking you no longer have the habit. You
could easily pick up the habit again, but right now, you're an
ex-smoker and likely to remain one. Sadly, 65 percent of those
who quit along with you three months ago are smoking.

Having been through the worst, you may now start to notice
the long-term rewards of not smoking, such as greater self-
esteem and energy. At best, ex-smokers find healthy substitutes
for their smoking habits—exercise, relaxation, assertive
behavior—which improves their well-being overall. You might
want to take a few moments to review the ways that your behavior has changed in the last three months. You could even,
if you're inclined, set goals for the next three months.

❖   ❖

*"To the extent that smoking constitutes a maladaptive response
for coping with stress and negative effects such as anxiety,
depression, anger, frustration, loneliness, or boredom,
the former smoker must find alternative strategies for
coping."*

—*"The Health Benefits of Smoking Cessation,"*
Surgeon General's Report, *1990*

| D A Y   9 4 | Even three months after quitting, when tobacco is supposed to be long gone from the system, some people still feel funny. Not much research has been done on this long-term withdrawal, but considering that the smoker's body has over years become acclimated to such chemicals as hydrogen-cyanide, formaldehyde, and radioactive polonium-210, it doesn't seem surprising that finding a new equilibrium could take time.

Ethan Rutherford, after three months, reported: "My body is doing some strange things. I'm having trouble cooling myself. My nerves are also involved, and I have itching sensations." As tobacco impedes circulation and constricts blood vessels, these responses aren't incredible.

Sabrina P. was exhausted: "All I could do was sleep for months." As nicotine is a stimulant and her body had been running on cigarettes for years, it was probably time to sleep.

Other people mention becoming ill often in the first six months after quitting. Again, the science here isn't strong, but perhaps inhaled poisons can inhibit the development of certain antibodies. Whatever the cause, one might well consider the first six months off cigarettes a period of recovery, during which the body is recuperating from a great and long trauma.

❖ ❖

"My sore throat is finally getting better. I'm getting my voice back. I did some recording recently and was pleased with what I heard."

—ETHAN RUTHERFORD, *singer, ex-smoker*

Besides the known smoking diseases, there are numerous

other annoyances of old age that are exacerbated by smoking. One of these is cataracts, the clouding of the lens of the eye afflicting more than a million Americans. Twice as many smokers (of a pack a day or more) as nonsmokers get cataracts. They are generally operable, but in the poor countries of the world, cataracts are the leading cause of blindness.

Ex-smokers apparently still carry some excess risk for cataracts, but light smokers very little. Researchers have not concluded how smoking affects cataracts, but one theory is that smoking reduces the levels of the nutrients that are important to maintaining clear lenses.

❖ ❖

Papal Ban: Pope Urban VIII, who occupied the Holy See from 1623–1644, declared that tobacco users in Seville would be excommunicated. Innocent XI renewed the order in 1681 and expanded it to apply to anyone taking tobacco in or about Saint Peter's in Rome. The papal opposition to tobacco was mainly ineffective, but still wasn't abandoned until 1725.

Cutting down on smoking is the favorite dream of many smokers. They consider life without cigarettes beyond imagining and cherish the thought of smoking only a few cigarettes a day—the ones that are satisfying—and dismissing the ones that make them feel lousy.

Some people actually manage to do this, and certainly less is better. But maintaining the reduced quota is problematical for a confirmed smoker. Either the struggle to smoke less is ongoing or in times of stress the old consumption level reasserts itself. For many nicotine addicts, cutting down doesn't work because withdrawal symptoms set in a few minutes after the last cigarette has been smoked. Stopping altogether in the end is much less painful than continuing the strain of rationing.

Some people do succeed as very light smokers. Their problem is that they are missing out on most of the benefits of being nonsmokers. They do reduce their mortality rates, but they don't feel great, they still respond to stress by smoking, they spend time thinking about cigarettes, and they have to worry about their cigarette supplies. Quitting is infinitely better.

❖ ❖

"Dixon paused in the portico to light the cigarette which, according to his schedule, he ought to be lighting after breakfast on the next day but one."

—KINGSLEY AMIS, Lucky Jim, 1953

Various studies have shown
that smoking weakens the im-

mune system. The system's first line of defense are the T-cells, which sound the alarm to bring other white blood cells to the rescue when disease strikes.

A 1989 study showed smoking linked with various changes in the T-cells, along with an overall increase in white blood cells. No appreciable differences were found between the T-cells of ex-smokers and nonsmokers, suggesting that the changes are reversible. However, other studies have been less encouraging in regard to ex-smokers.

A Russian study demonstrated a decrease in T-cells in long-time smokers. This Russian study also tested for antibodies to tuberculosis and found two to three times more negativity among the smokers. As this was a population with considerable exposure to tuberculosis, the inference was that the smokers' immune systems, which should have produced antibodies, were deficient.

Immunoglobulins, which protect against invading substances, are another component of the immune system. In tests of smokers' saliva, these have been found to be reduced, with the numbers consistent with the amount of smoking. In ex-smokers, the concentrations had returned to normal.

❖ ❖

THE ODDS: In a study of HIV-infected men, smokers were twice as likely to develop AIDS during a fifty-six month observation period as the nonsmokers.

| D A Y   9 8 | Good health habits and bad ones cluster together, and

smokers often flunk numerous tests of healthy living, whereas former smokers tend to clean up in other departments besides smoking. Ex-smokers are not only more likely to exercise regularly than smokers, they drink less, eat less fat, and get more sleep. In fact, quitters who increase their levels of exercise are more likely to remain quitters. Smokers are more likely to drink and drive than ex-smokers and are less inclined to use their seat belts.

Despite the studies, it remains anybody's guess as to whether former smokers do better because they were more motivated toward health in the first place or because quitting smoking inspired them to plow forward in yet more healthful directions. To you, it doesn't matter, for you have already thrown your hat into the ring with the healthy cluster.

❖   ❖

"While assigned to radiation therapy in 1947, I met my boyhood hero [Babe Ruth]. The Babe was . . . receiving radiation therapy for a large inoperable cancer at the back of his throat that was clearly the result of prolonged use of chewing tobacco, snuff, cigars, and alcohol . . . he smiled and, as we shook hands, said, "Hello, Doc" in a hoarse whisper; the radiation treatments had begun to inflame his vocal cords." (Babe Ruth the great home run hitter, died at age 52 of lung, throat, liver, and lung cancer.)
—WILLIAM G. CAHAN, M.D., No Stranger to Tears, 1992

Considering the exposure of a smoker's mouth to smoke, one

should not be surprised by damage to the teeth and gums. Indeed, studies substantiate that smokers have a high ratio of periodontal (gum) disease—according to one study four times as much as nonsmokers. What's more, the smokers get it worse.

To add insult to injury, surgery doesn't come out so well with the smokers. One study comparing smokers and nonsmokers discovered that the pocket reductions for smokers a year after surgery were only three-fifths those of the nonsmokers. Gum problems result from the effects of tobacco in the bloodstream as well as from smoke in the mouth.

Now that you're a nonsmoker, your gums won't heal overnight, but at least any time and trouble you put into them is much less likely to be wasted.

❖   ❖

"Quite a few periodontists won't even do certain procedures on smokers because smoking interferes with healing."
                                            —DR. LARY SCHILLER, *periodontist*

| D A Y   1 0 0 | One of the finest habits any ex-addict can develop is that of taking a nap. Napping is nice for anyone, but because addicts go in for mood change, they often neglect rest in favor of artificial stimulation. But a small nap can be the best response to a problem, invariably producing a brighter outlook and a more sensible response. Of course, many of us have no inclination to take naps. When tired, our instinct is to whip ourselves on with a cup of coffee or a cigarette. We often don't even recognize fatigue when we have it, nor hold any hope of actual midday sleep. But even when sleep is out of the question, a short lie-down brings a resurgence of real energy.

You already know the importance of a good night's sleep. The tired person loses judgment, and slips in judgment are smoke and fire to the person just 100 days from his or her last cigarette. And congratulations. This is an anniversary worth celebrating. Perhaps with a nap?

A Smoker's Life: A 1988 study at the University of Michigan found that smokers tend to sleep less, fight more, and take more risks.

Boredom is a big reason for smoking, and if your life feels emptier now that you don't smoke, you should be looking for things to fill it up with. Even people with very busy lives can be deeply bored if their days seem like endless drudgery. As Socrates remarked, the unexamined life is not worth living, so you might want to take a look at your life in terms of what you're getting out of it. This isn't just general life advice; it's a key to not smoking.

Most people aren't in a position to drop everything and sail single-handedly around the world in order to enliven their days, but small ingredients, such as a weekly yoga class, can make a big difference. If there's something you've always wanted to do, but never had the time, do a little bit of it. There's always some corner you can operate in.

And don't forget volunteer work. The satisfaction of helping an illiterate adult learn to read (call 800-228-8813), of delivering food to disabled people, or of being a Big Brother, are incalculable. And should you be thinking of a new career, volunteer work is often the place to start.

❖ ❖

"Believing we do something when we do nothing is the first illusion of tobacco."

—RALPH WALDO EMERSON

| D A Y   1 0 2 | The root cause of Sudden Infant Death Syndrome (SIDS)—

when a healthy baby is inexplicably found dead in its crib—remains a mystery. However, two doctors in Sweden discovered a strong link between SIDS and smoking in a study of 279,000 infants.

These doctors found that women who smoked only moderately while pregnant (1–9 cigarettes a day) were more than twice as likely as nonsmokers to lose an infant to SIDS. Women who smoked heavily (rated as 10-plus cigarettes a day) tripled their risk of having a baby succumb to SIDS.

The overall number of infant deaths was 0.7 per 1,000 live births. Among smokers, it was 1.47 per 1,000 live births. The Swedish doctors found other factors affecting the statistics, such as socioeconomic status and presence of a father, but nothing that weighed as heavily as the mother's smoking habits.

YOU'VE COME THE WRONG WAY, BABY: Women in developing countries are rapidly acquiring the smoking habit. Worldwide, women are now smoking in record numbers.

"When you've quit smoking, everything you do becomes

new because you're doing it without cigarettes," notes Julie Smith. This can actually be exciting, if only for the novelty of discovering that you can face crises, talk on the telephone, go to parties, and balance your checking account without smoking.

But new situations can be upsetting. Probably you used to smoke if something made you mad. What do you do now? Exploding is not constructive. Saying nothing makes you mad at yourself. That leaves the middle ground, currently known as "assertive behavior."

While "assertive behavior" can be an excuse for rudeness, it more properly is used as the exercise of one's own right to live. If everyone always leaves you to empty the garbage, assertive behavior requires that you politely let others know that you have other ideas. This does not mean you have to go around in a paranoid manner looking for ways in which you've been gypped—only that you speak up when you're reasonably certain that your cause is good. Self-assertion can be frightening if it's not your style and you're new at it, but like not smoking, you get better at it with practice.

❖ ❖

"It does not pay to smoke . . . I can work better and longer than before. I have less headache. I have a better opinion of myself. . . . I think I am rather better tempered, as well as more cheerful and satisfied."

—JAMES PARTON,
Does It Pay to Smoke and Drink? *1868*

| D A Y   1 0 4 | In past centuries, smoking was widely considered morally

wrong. Seventeenth-century shops selling tobacco were places of low repute, associated with brothels. Gentlemen did not smoke in the company of ladies, and ladies did not smoke at all.

Our present age does not allow much talk of morals; we prefer "choice." Few people would try to tell young people not to take up smoking because it's "wrong." Instead, we emphasize that it's "unhealthy." Yet an element of moral disapproval remains. Nonsmokers see in smokers a lack of self-discipline. The squandering of health, time, and money goes against our ideals.

One college study found that when students were told that the heroine of a story was a smoker they downgraded her on many levels. They found her less "socially attractive," less healthy, a poorer student, less disciplined, less gentle, and less wise.

❖ ❖

"I know in this Country many of my friends much given to Tobacco, but when I ask them what profit they receive of it, they say none; Nevertheless, they cannot leave it for customs' sake or wantonness."

—MATTHIAS DE L'OBEL, **Perfuming of Tobacco, 1611**

In looking back, ex-smokers

are often appalled to recall
how low cigarettes dragged them. More than a few can remember occasions when they scoured the sidewalks looking
for smokable butts, generally during quitting periods. Then
there were the midnight junkets to a 7-Eleven six miles away to
replenish supplies. Shy people, sitting in train stations, become
desperate enough to ask strangers for cigarettes. Husbands tell
their wives and wives their husbands that they're walking to the
store, then hide in the alley smoking. And cigarettes are always listed under necessities on the shopping list, although
there may be no money left to bring home a watermelon for the
kiddies.

Very nice people do all these things. Victims of addiction
are driven by forces beyond their control. The only cure is the
road you've taken—to quit smoking.

❖ ❖

*"When I smoked my self-control went right down the drain,
along with my self-respect."*
—LAWRENCE TELLONE, *New York City cabdriver and ex-smoker*

Osteoporosis—a thinning of the bones—is one of the great threats of old age. Thin bones break, and hip fractures among the elderly often spell the end of independent living. Smokers suffer much more from osteoporosis than nonsmokers.

A number of studies have shown postmenopausal smokers losing significantly greater amounts of bone mass than nonsmokers. A Swedish study of women discovered that the smokers had 15 to 30 percent less bone mass than nonsmokers. Another study found pack years a significant predictor of bone mass.

There are various theories as to why smokers lose bone mass. Smokers go through menopause earlier than nonsmokers, which extends the period of susceptibility. Furthermore, smoking may reduce the production of estrogens and/or the effectiveness of estrogen therapy. It may also be that smokers don't absorb calcium well. Possibly, the increased rate of osteoporosis in smokers could be only because smokers exercise less. But a Norwegian study found inactive smokers had four times the hip fractures of inactive nonsmokers and concluded that important as exercise is, it's not by any means as important as not smoking.

❖   ❖

"Many women use smoking as a coping strategy, for example to create a 'space' in a day filled with the stress of bringing up children and having to face different types of work, often with little social support and on a low income. Environments need to be created which enable them to break free of this health-damaging behavior."
—AMANDA AMOS AND CLAIRE CHOLLAT TARQUET,
World Health, 1990

Tobacco was the economic salvation of the colony of Vir-

ginia, which had been a miserable failure until John Rolfe—the fellow who married Pocahontas—figured out how to grow and cure marketable Virginia tobacco. Before that, all fine tobacco came from the Caribbean and South America.

James I, king of England from 1603 to 1625, despised smoking and raged against the habit. He maintained that no successful colony could be built upon smoke; nonetheless, by 1627 Virginia was exporting a half million pounds of tobacco a year. In 1619, James had prohibited the growing of tobacco on English soil—a favorable move for the colonies because it removed domestic competition. It was also a profitable move for the Crown because the duties on imported tobacco were high.

❖ ❖

"And surely in my opinion, there cannot be a more base, and yet hurtful, corruption in a country, than is the vile use (or rather abuse) of taking Tobacco in this kingdom."
—JAMES I OF ENGLAND, 1604

Whether or not cigarette advertising actually *makes* people smoke is debatable. But it is clear that the bad news about smoking leads people to not smoke. This bad news does not get out as loudly and clearly as it should, even in this era of tobacco bashing.

For instance: In March of 1990, R. J. Reynolds launched a new cigarette brand in Houston, Texas. It was a brand designed to attract young women. An organization called Doctors Ought to Care (DOC) created a countercampaign with ads that pointed out that smoking these, or any, cigarettes led to the grave.

The new brand was called Dakota, and the DOC ads used the slogan "Dakota, DaCough, DaCancer, DaCoffin." DOC's ads ran in the local weeklies, but the two major city dailies refused to carry them—they did not wish to offend their cigarette advertisers.

❖ ❖

SORRY FACT: The number of high school girls who smoke (12.5 percent) has not diminished, and high school girls now smoke more than high school boys.

At age 83, Sigmund Freud died of cancer after 45 years

of unsuccessfully trying to give up smoking cigars. His advanced age at death might give hope to smokers were it not for the agony of the last 21 years of his life, spent undergoing operations for cancer of the palate and jaw. By the age of 79, according to one account: "His jaw had been entirely removed and an artificial jaw substituted; he was in almost constant pain; often he could not chew or swallow. Yet at the age of 81 he was still smoking an endless series of cigars."

Living long and miserably is almost as great a threat to the smoker as dying young. Age has its price for healthy people, and the price is higher for old smokers. They are the ones whose lives are most likely to be narrowed by long lists of debilities. Many stroke victims, alive but paralyzed and speechless, were once smokers.

THE BRIGHTER SIDE: Ten years after quitting smoking, the risk of getting cancer of the mouth or throat returns to that of a nonsmoker.

| D A Y   1 1 0 | Tobacco was immediately so profitable a crop in colonial

Virginia that once the settlers discovered it they were loath to plant anything else. New buildings weren't built and grains weren't grown. The governor, John Smith, objected to the cultivation of tobacco and the sight of "our men rooting in the ground about tobacco like swine. . . . For discoveries they have made none, nor any other commodity than tobacco do they apply themselves unto."

Even John Rolfe, credited with developing the methods that made Virginia tobacco possible, warned the people not to "spend too much of their time and labor in planting tobacco, known to them to be very vendible in England, and so neglect their tillage of corn and fall into want thereof." A law was finally passed that no farmer could plant tobacco at all unless he had planted two acres of corn for himself and two for every manservant.

SHAMEFUL COMMERCE: The Dutch brought the first African slaves to America in 1619. The Virginians paid for them with the only coin they had—tobacco.

Anyone with an ulcer who continues smoking is pitiable. Or

needs a new doctor. A doctor who doesn't tell an ulcer patient to stop smoking isn't reading his medical journals. The 1980s were notable for conclusive research regarding smoking and ulcers.

These studies confirmed the long-held hypothesis that smokers have higher maximal acid output than nonsmokers, and a 1989 French investigation established a linear relationship between acid output and the number of cigarettes smoked per day. With unusual consistency, numerous other studies showed that smokers suffer high rates of ulcers, more complications, and low rates of healing. However, once smokers stop smoking, they respond rapidly to treatment. In a Japanese study of 40 smoking ulcer patients, eleven of the twelve who quit smoking were pronounced completely healed in twelve weeks. Of the 28 still smoking, only seven had healed. Such results have been repeated many times.

The mortality rate for peptic ulcers has declined rapidly during the past several decades, paralleling the decrease in smoking. Those who still smoke stand three to four times the chance of dying from peptic, duodenal, or gastric ulcers as nonsmokers. (Smokers, however, may take hope from recent discoveries showing the effectiveness of antibiotics in curing ulcers.)

❖   ❖

THE ODDS: *In a study of ulcer patients not taking medicine, 72 percent of smokers had recurrences versus 21 percent of nonsmokers.*

```
D A Y   1 1 2
```
Most smokers start smoking as teenagers, with the idea that smoking is sophisticated. The first few cigarettes are usually sickening, and some initiates become nonsmokers forthwith. Others persevere until they can smoke without nausea, faintness, or coughing fits. As they mature, they come to hate the smoking habit they went to such effort to acquire.

Nonetheless, most ever-smokers still harbor buried associations between cigarettes and romance, glamour, hope, and rebellion. Somewhere in your youth there was likely to have been a figure you admired extravagantly who smoked. Hypnotherapists have some luck at digging up these associations and say that holding them up to the light helps to squish them.

If not smoking continues to be unduly difficult for you, you might want some help digging around in your psyche. Or, instead, you might try just lying down on your own couch and letting your mind meander along the old cigarette trails. Imagine how you actually looked smoking as a kid: gangly, chubby, or babyish, pretending a maturity you would never get from puffing on cigarettes.

❖   ❖

When asked how he came to be so prodigious a smoker, Charles Lamb replied, "I toiled after it, Sir, as some men toil after virtue."

—THE LETTERS OF CHARLES LAMB, *1895*

Sidestream smoke is chemically different from the smoke

that is inhaled. The smoker inhales the large particles; the non-smoker (as well as the smoker) gets a mixture of irritating gases and small carcinogenic tar particles that come from the burning end of the cigarette. This stuff reaches deep into the lungs, and because of incomplete combustion, is even dirtier than mainstream smoke.

It's estimated that sidestream smoke causes 3,700 deaths from heart disease each year. The effect of sidestream smoke is to make platelets—which make the blood clot—stickier. Stickier platelets lead to more clots in the arteries. One of the reasons for the clotting is that tobacco smoke seems to injure cells on the inside lining of the arteries, and platelets are more likely to stick on damaged cells.

Furthermore, passive smokers have a decrease in oxygen in their blood, thus impeding exercise. There are suspicions that sidestream smoke upsets enzyme activity within cells, which may contribute to reduced heart function. For people who already have heart problems, exposure to smoke may give rise to the severe pain of angina.

❖ ❖

"[Tobacco] much indisposes us for business."
—HUMPHREY BROOKE, The Durable Legacy, 1681

| D A Y   1 1 4 | Infertile couples intensify their difficulties by smoking. Smok-

ers have lower fertility to begin with, due to the various effects of tobacco—hormonal imbalance and irregular menstrual cycles are just a couple. For marginally fertile couples, the length of the delay in conceiving corresponds with the amount of smoking.

Should the couple resort to in vitro (test tube) fertilization, their chances of success are impaired by either prospective parent's smoking, according to at least one clinic's analysis. The smoking woman produces fewer eggs; the sperm of the smoking man is less able to penetrate the egg. What's more, the smoking man has a reduced sperm count. Once pregnant, if either prospective parent smokes, the chances of a miscarriage increase by 64 percent.

❖   ❖

"[Tobacco causes] sterility and barrenness ... it seemeth an enemy to the life of man."
—PHILARETES, **Work for Chimney-Sweepers,** *1601*

There is a growing body of evidence demonstrating that

smokers produce children with reduced mental capacities. One might be tempted to dismiss the test results on the grounds that less educated people smoke more; however, even when adjusting for background, smokers' children test out with poorer concentration, less cognitive ability, and lower IQs. These differences are very mild, but are apparent even for siblings whose mothers smoked during one pregnancy and not during the other.

Children whose fathers rather than mothers smoked during pregnancy also have underaverage scores on tests of speech, language, motor skills, and behavior. It seems possible that nicotine affects the fetal brain in critical stages of development.

❖   ❖

DYING TO SMOKE: In Sarajevo, smokers wait in line for many hours to buy cigarettes—in an area susceptible to shelling—spending all their disposable income on cigarettes. A married couple interviewed by National Public Radio explained that it was because their child smoked as well as themselves that they were willing to risk their lives for cigarettes.

| D A Y   1 1 6 | Thirty or forty years ago, when cigarettes were in their heyday, glamour consisted of Humphrey Bogart and Lauren Bacall in a cloud of smoke. Audrey Hepburn's ultimate touch of sophistication in *Breakfast at Tiffany's* was her long cigarette holder. Today it's hard to understand how alluring Bette Davis, Joan Crawford, Clark Gable, Katharine Hepburn, John Barrymore, and Marlene Dietrich once looked blowing smoke.

"I smoked; everybody smoked," says director Blake Edwards. Then times changed. Bogie died of cancer of the esophagus in 1957 at age 57. Lung cancer got John Wayne. Edwards now says he can't stand to be around smokers. Donald Sutherland and other stars request that smokers stay clear of the set; many movie sets are smoke free.

Smoking still has its place in movies—to portray sons of bitches, rebels, depressives, psychopaths, and troublemakers. Or to signal problems ahead. In *Regarding Henry*, Harrison Ford steps out for a pack of cigarettes and gets shot. Just a little joke from screenwriter Jeffrey Abrams, who hates smoking.

❖ ❖

"Smoking is one of the most grievous examples of destructive behavior in the history of mankind."
—CHARLES LEMAISTRE,
former president of the American Cancer Society

Pelvic inflammatory disease (PID) is one more affliction that

occurs more commonly in smokers than nonsmokers. PID is an infection of the fallopian tubes that mainly strikes young women and is a frequent cause of infertility.

A 1990 study examined the relationship between smoking and PID by questioning 197 women hospitalized with their first episodes of the disease. As controls, 667 women hospitalized for unrelated problems were compared. The researchers adjusted for confounding factors, such as the number of recent sexual partners.

Compared with never-smokers, current smokers had a 1.7 times greater incidence of PID. The researchers were not prepared to state a definite cause-and-effect relationship without further investigation, but there is no ready explanation other than a causal one.

❖ ❖

YOU'VE COME THE WRONG WAY, BABY: Women are dying in greater numbers than ever before from smoking. In the United States more women annually die of lung cancer (51,000) than of breast cancer (44,500). Pancreatic cancer claims 13,200 women a year. Smokers have high rates of cervical cancer, and some researchers suspect a link between smoking and ovarian and uterine cancer. Teenage girls are smoking as much as ever.

Artistic circles have often been wreathed in clouds of smoke, due possibly to either craziness or creativity or both. Helen-Maria Erawan took up smoking when she arrived in Montreal as a young actress: "I was surrounded by aspirants in the theater who wanted to look dashing and in their extreme nervousness needed props. I felt smoking made me look sophisticated.

"Later, living in New York City and working in a tiny publishing house in Greenwich Village, I would smoke all day long. I always had a great feeling of peace when I smoked. Physically, I felt very well, and I was pleasantly conscious of my rather gravelly contralto voice.

"Secretly, I was really cheesed off when I felt morally compelled to quit. My husband and I were making documentary films, and we initially quit for political reasons—a protest against tobacco companies. He quit cold turkey. I went on sneaking cigarettes for two years. But we had children, and for that reason I knew I just had to stop. It was very hard, especially because I was turning out a lot of scripts then and had the idea that smoking did wonders for my writing. But two years after I quit altogether, I noticed that I'd really been very productive since stopping, and we had delivered a number of rather good films to PBS. So smoking clearly wasn't essential."

❖   ❖

"I advise nonsmokers to avoid exposure to cigarette smoke wherever possible, and . . . in particular, they should protect infants and children from this smoke."
                    —C. EVERETT KOOP, *former U.S. Surgeon General*

Scientific proof of the link be-

tween smoking and deadly dis-
ease was slow in coming, but long before the famous Surgeon General's Report of 1964, anyone with a little common sense could see that smoking didn't do anyone any good. Smoking was considered a disgusting habit long before the damning scientific evidence was in.

John McConnell, now of Glendale, New York, remembers being taken to Portales, New Mexico, as a lad in about 1930 to hear Tommy Ryan speak. Ryan was a world-renowned athlete, a former world middleweight champion. At the time, Chesterfield cigarettes had persuaded various athletes to testify that they smoked Chesterfields without any effect on their lung power. Ryan instead promised $200 to any two-pack-a-dayer who could bench press 200 pounds. "All the cowpunchers stepped up," says McConnell, "but nobody got that $200. Then Ryan did it himself with one arm." Ryan never smoked himself, and McConnell never forgot the lesson and never smoked either.

❖   ❖

A SMOKER'S LIFE: A health agency survey found that smokers were less active than nonsmokers, less inclined to use seat belts, more apt to be heavy, and more likely to have poor diets.

Filtered cigarettes were the answer to the cancer scare of the 1950's. Until then, filters were a negligible part of the market, but lung cancer studies were giving both smokers and the industry something to worry about.

Lorillard launched Kent cigarettes in 1952 with a big health promotion. Buyers came in droves but didn't stick around; the filter was too effective, making Kents unsatisfactory smokes. In 1956, Lorillard quietly fixed the filter to let through more tar and nicotine.

Marlboros came out in 1954 with an advertising campaign designed to counter the impression that filters were sissy—a campaign so successful that Marlboros are now the world's most popular cigarette. Indeed, there is nothing sissy about filters. Some deliver as big a tar/nicotine blast as nonfilters. And people who switch to genuinely low tar and nicotine cigarettes usually satisfy their addiction by smoking more cigarettes.

As filter material is even cheaper than tobacco, filter cigarettes provided the cigarette industry with a bonanza. Filter smokers do have a lower lung cancer risk, but only marginally. On bladder cancer rates, filtered cigarettes have no effect.

❖   ❖

"I'm dying proof that smoking will kill you."
—WAYNE MCLAREN, *former Marlboro Man,*
died of lung cancer in 1992

The nicotine skin patch is a wonderful help in reducing the

pain of nicotine withdrawal. But as one failed quitter says, "It's great but it's not a magic bullet."

Patch people face the same problems all quitters do—a quickening of emotions, the loss of a constant companion, a struggle to change habits. These all pass in time, but in having escaped some early anguish, patch people can be lulled into a false security.

The above-mentioned quitter says that with each switch to a lower level of nicotine, she was irritable for twenty-four hours and then adjusted. But when she took off the last patch she became so irrationally hostile that she thought she was having a nervous breakdown. One weekend night when she was home alone, feeling depressed, she searched her handbag collection until she found three cigarettes. Within a few weeks she was back to two packs a day.

She's coughing again and regretful. Next time she's going to join a program and line up a support group. She's down but not out.

❖   ❖

"The wretcheder one is, the more one smokes; and the more one smokes, the wretcheder one gets—a vicious cycle!"
—GEORGE LOUIS PALMELLA, **Peter Ibbetson**, *1891*

Smokers, in general not less well mannered than other people, can become ferociously rude where smoking is concerned. The author of *War and Peace*, Leo Tolstoy, blames tobacco itself for provoking the degrading behavior.

❖ ❖

"The observation as to what extent smoking drowns the voice of conscience may be made on almost any smoker. Every smoker, in surrendering himself to his passion, forgets or neglects the very first demands of social life, which he ... observes in all other cases, as long as his conscience is not drowned by tobacco. Every man of our medium degree of education regards it as impermissible, rude, and inhuman for his own pleasure to impair the quiet and the comfort, and much more the health, of other people. Nobody will permit himself to wet a room in which people are sitting, to be noisy, yell, to let in cold, hot, or foul air, to commit acts which interfere with others or harm them. But not one of a thousand smokers will feel any embarrassment at filling with foul air a room, the air of which non-smoking women and children breathe. Even though smokers usually ask "Does it incommode you?" all know that these persons are supposed to answer, "Not in the least."

—LEO TOLSTOY, Why People Become Intoxicated, *1890*

Dr. William Weis, a professor of business at Seattle University, recommends to all businesses that they ban smoking. He contends that it's not only a legal obligation to protect employees' health but the only sound economic policy.

1. Smokers are absent 50 percent more than nonsmokers.
2. Smokers spend time smoking. Smokers will universally insist that they work at least as hard as nonsmokers, but research is producing evidence of lower productivity among smoking employees.
3. Insurance costs are higher for smokers. Some insurers offer up to 45 percent deductions for term life coverage for nonsmokers.
4. Some studies show smokers have more accidental injuries.
5. Health and fire premiums can go down 35 percent for smoke-free businesses.
6. Disability and early retirement costs can be cut. Smokers are six times more likely to become disabled and retire early.
7. Air-conditioning requirements are two to three times greater where people smoke. Filters must be changed much more frequently.
8. Building maintenance costs plunge when smoking is banned. Many chores once done monthly can be done semiannually.

❖   ❖

"The effect on employee morale is the highest cost of all. As long as you have smoking, you're going to have conflict."
—PROFESSOR WILLIAM WEIS, *Seattle University*

| D A Y   1 2 4 | Suzanne Mantell gave up her cigarettes at the start of a three-week car trip with a nonsmoking friend. Camping through the Southeast, Mantell was surprised at how little she missed her cigarettes: "Cigarettes had been a companion for me, a good friend, and as I had a replacement companion during the trip, I wasn't lonely without my cigarettes. By the time I got home, I was able to get along without them."

There are other positive elements to the travel-and-quit technique:

1. You've changed your routine and escaped the daily triggers that signal smoking time.
2. Ideally, you're in as stress-free a situation as you could hope for. Away from phone calls, jobs, pressures, and housework, all you need to do is get up in the morning and move the car down the road.
3. You've not only got a companion, you've got a warden. When traveling with another person, you're unlikely to get away from that person long enough to start smoking.

Vacation quitting should not be confused with its less promising variation: globetrotting. For quitting, you don't want pressure and excitement. Quitting vacations should be undemanding, with lots of time for taking it easy.

❖   ❖

"I write, and it always seemed lonely and frightening to me to step onto the blank page by myself. With cigarettes I wasn't alone. But I still write, and I do it without smoking."

—SUZANNE MANTELL, *ex-smoker*

In 1617, Joshuah Sylvester declared that of the two smoky inventions in his age—guns and tobacco pipes—tobacco was the more deadly. Guns, he said, at least shot forward at the foe, "but tobacco pipes attack their own, poisoning their users."

Under the circumstances, it is questionable whether cigarette advertising should be legal. Other than weapons, cigarettes are the only consumer goods that have no safe use and are dangerous even when used in moderation. Cigarette ads are wholly deceptive, depicting smokers as healthy people having jolly times.

The worst of tobacco advertising is that it consciously casts a net out to youngsters, the future market. So the most susceptible consumers, the ones who could still be saved from becoming smokers, absorb the message that smoking is a fun thing to do. Cigarette companies claim that their advertising mission is only to attract brand switchers, an unlikely story because brand loyalty is very strong among smokers.

❖ ❖

"Replenishing the pool of customers is especially important for cigarettes, since they kill 350,000 people each year, other smokers die from natural causes, and many quit each year."

—LARRY C. WHITE, **Merchants of Death**, *1988*

Ultimately, it is the nicotine and not the advertising that hooks people. Once hooked, smokers don't need advertising to keep them smoking, but they are almost certainly more likely to start because of it.

The New Zealand Toxic Substances Board concluded after extensive study that the more control a government had over tobacco advertising and promotion, the greater the annual average fall in tobacco use in adults and young people. In December of 1990, New Zealand banned cigarette advertising. Tobacco consumption rapidly dropped 15 percent and is still going down.

Short of banning all cigarette advertising, it might be reasonable to condemn it to the "tombstone" (no pictures, no color) format now required for many ads for stocks and bonds. The tombstone format protects financial investors from being swayed by appeals to emotion; children should have at least this much protection from something far more lethal than bum investments.

❖ ❖

"People my age aren't thinking about dying, and I never paid any attention to the warnings on cigarette packs. Then I took care of my grandfather when he was dying of emphysema. After that, my mother and I both quit smoking."

—SHANNON, *age 19, ex-smoker*

A smoker's risk for smoking diseases rises with the number of

cigarettes smoked. Statistics generally average all smokers
together—thus scaring some too much and some too little. The
average risk is lowered by the people who count as smokers
despite an almost negligible smoking habit. What is surprising
to many, however, is the definition of a heavy smoker. While
most individuals smoking a half pack a day would imagine
themselves light smokers, some studies make ten cigarettes a
day the cutoff point between "light" and "heavy."

Also significant is the number of years the habit has been
going on. For some diseases the lifetime number of cigarettes
counts for more than in others, but on the whole the risk is cumulative. The cumulative risk is often expressed in pack years:
packs per day times years of smoking. Numerous studies, however, do not distinguish between the size of the habit and the
lifetime consumption.

*Fatal Curve: The premature mortality risk of smokers by
number of cigarettes smoked per day: less than ten per day:
1.29; 10 to 20 per day: 1.67; 21 to 39 per day: 2.03;
40 or more per day: 2.36.*

| D A Y   1 2 8 |

Tobacco farms use phosphate fertilizers, which contain traces of uranium 235. Uranium 235 ends up as polonium in the tobacco plant's leaves. When the tobacco is smoked, these polonium particles settle in the lungs and bronchi—a possible cause of cancer. In autopsies, 93 percent of smokers are found to have abnormal, metaplastic cells in their lungs.

Lung cancer rates skyrocket when other carcinogens, such as asbestos, are combined with smoking. Nonsmoking asbestos workers have three or four times the normal rate of lung cancer; smoking asbestos workers have a rate 30 times normal. Households with high radon levels are at much greater risk for lung cancer if there's smoking going on in them.

Most lung cancers cannot be diagnosed early. By the time someone develops symptoms, the cancer has usually begun to spread. The five-year survival rate for lung cancer is 13 percent.

AN EARLY GRAVE: Eddie Kendricks, a founding member and lead singer of the Temptations singing group, died of lung cancer on October 5, 1992. He was 52 years old and had smoked for thirty years. Before he died, he urged children to never start to smoke.

People who have been smoking for 40 or 50 years often imagine that they've beaten the odds and are immune to smokers' diseases or that the damage is already done and it's too late to stop.

Nothing could be further from the truth. The longer you've smoked, the higher your risk for disease, and even people who die in car crashes, happily smoking, are losers. Old smokers are not enjoying either the mental or bodily fitness that they could be. Old smokers suffer additionally because many medications are less effective combined with tobacco, even when given in larger doses.

What do you now have to show for your four smokefree months? At the very least your circulation is better, your airways are in the process of repair, and you can breathe more deeply. If you don't have more energy yet, be patient. You will. All these things are true whether you're eighteen or eighty.

❖ ❖

"I went to visit Alice, my old schoolmate, who's almost 75 now. She's gotten Burger's disease from smoking and is in a wheelchair. She had a coughing fit just as I arrived. She sat beside me on the couch, and I had to repeat most of what I said as she's a bit deaf. Then she lit up a cigarette, coughed some more, and we had a good talk. With difficulty she got up and into her wheelchair to go to the bathroom. To put it mildly, she's a wreck. I can hardly see how the joy of smoking could be worth the consequences for her.'"

—Dr. Patricia Watson

Mary Pana got in nearly 50 years of smoking before the day she tried to call to a passing woodseller from her porch. "I couldn't call out. Instead, this sort of bray emerged." She had already moved from the soprano to the tenor section of her choral group; she'd also noticed that when she answered the phone, her "hello" no longer had the old upward swoop. She saw the handwriting on the wall and made an appointment with a throat doctor.

"He looked down my throat and said, 'Well, young lady, you're home free, but don't ever smoke another cigarette.' " I had a vocal cord that was all bumpy and probably precancerous."

Her approach to quitting was unusual. "I said to myself, 'Tonight I'm going to make the best martini I've ever had, and I'm going to enjoy it without a cigarette. Tomorrow morning I will make the world's finest pot of coffee, which I will drink with all the pleasure that coffee alone has to offer."

It worked. (It wouldn't work for everybody.) Mrs. Pana never smoked again. Her voice can again swoop right up to a high F. "You just ride through the urge to smoke," she recommends. "I used to think of labor pains. You take a deep breath and wait until it's over. And don't go in for substitutes, like chewing gum and candy. Just ride it through."

❖ ❖

DYING FOR A SMOKE: In any given year, a smoker has a 68 percent greater chance of dying than a nonsmoker. Rates for heavy smokers are about double that.

Statistics sometimes show men
as more successful in laying off

cigarettes than women. Hmm, we wonder, could the weaker
sex really be weaker? And then it turns out that a number of
these men have forsworn cigarettes in favor of cigars or the
pipe.

This is certainly not what this book has in mind. Somebody
who is sitting around fouling the air with tobacco smoke of any
kind is no success story. This is a man who has lowered his risk
of pulmonary disease (if he doesn't inhale), but not one who
has embarked on a new and vigorous life.

Incidentally, other kinds of smoking may also be unwise.
Marijuana is a pitfall for ex-smokers. Not only is smoking marijuana a step toward smoking cigarettes, but the marijuana-
fogged mind is not prepared to contest when the urge for a
cigarette follows the smoking of a joint. This may not be true for
some people, but there's a phalanx of ex-ex-smokers ready to
testify that dope smoking was their undoing.

❖   ❖

*"I hadn't smoked for four months. Then I smoked a smidgen
of marijuana and thought, 'Boy, a cigarette sure would be
nice.' I got hold of one, and here I am again at two packs
a day."*

—ANON., 1992

"Why do people smoke?" is the question to which David Krogh has devoted most of his book, *The Artificial Passion*.

Smokers can rarely provide a good answer. It's not the taste, not the high, not even the pleasure. Says Krogh: "To the casual, nonsmoking observer, it's as if smokers have gotten the worst of both worlds: drug addiction without drug euphoria."

It's not even the pull of nicotine addiction. All those people smoking while wearing nicotine patches can attest to that. They're getting their nicotine but they want to smoke.

Krogh comes up with reasons aplenty to explain why people who aren't crazy like to smoke. Many are little reasons but they combine into something big. One little reason is that smoking is as close as a person can come to doing nothing while still doing something. "Human beings may be incapable of doing absolutely nothing, but they don't mind coming close, and smoking can fit into this narrow space quite well."

❖ ❖

"I have often wished that every individual of the human race afflicted with this artificial passion could prevail on himself to try but for three months the experiment which I have made; sure that it would turn every acre of tobacco land into a wheat field and add ten years of longevity to the average human life."

—JOHN Q. ADAMS (1767–1848)

As an addictive drug, nicotine is an oddity because it doesn't

produce euphoria or visions or the sort of uplift that would seem to make the game worth the candle. Instead, according to David Krogh, author of *The Artificial Passion*, people seem to smoke to get normal.

Nicotine soothes mood swings and can bring people back to an average feeling from a variety of other states—such as boredom, anger, and irritation. For instance, in a six-hour driving experiment, everybody's fatigue and concentration decreased, but the nonsmokers also grew more aggressive and lost "social warmth." Not so the smokers.

This mood control is a poor reason to smoke, but it's a reason. In the long run, though, smokers will end up more bored, angry, and stressed than nonsmokers. The nonsmokers will probably have enough sense never to do that dumb driving experiment again, whereas the smokers will get right back in the car and smoke another pack of cigarettes.

And in the meanwhile, what do you do about boredom and stress, etc.? You just hang on. Perhaps these emotions are telling you something worth hearing.

The Nicotine Bullet: Nicotine takes 8 seconds to reach the brain and 15 to 20 seconds to reach the big toe.

| D A Y   1 3 4 | "I smoked two and a half packs a day for 27 years,"

says Stefan S., "and I always hated the loss of freedom. Then it became worse and worse being the only smoker among health-oriented people. I run seminars, and a lot of the business at these things gets done during the breaks, but the only thing that got done for me was sneaking out back and smoking." And then I'd use breath spray and try to keep a distance from people when I came back."

Stefan quit by going to Nicotine Anonymous. "I went to three meetings a week for nearly a year. I realized I'd have to pull out all the stops to quit, but I was willing to. I knew it wasn't just a nasty little habit. I'd seen my mother die of lung cancer at the age of 62. I once figured that I'd spent about three and half million minutes of my life smoking. I could put some time into quitting.

"A lot has changed. My whole relationship to the planet is different because I spend so much time outdoors. Emotionally I'm much more aware. Smoking is an anesthetic for feelings; I was stunted while I smoked."

❖ ❖

EARLY GRAVES: A recent documentary showed a clip of Edward R. Murrow interviewing Nat King Cole. Both were smoking. Both men died of lung cancer, Murrow at age 56, Cole at only 45.

Stroke has become more the province of smokers than it

used to be. This is partly because those who took up smoking in great numbers decades back are now paying their dues. It is also because the incidence of stroke has declined overall, probably because of techniques of controlling hypertension—techniques that are less effective among smokers.

The more encouraging news is that quitting smoking rapidly lowers the risk of strokes. While studies vary, several large ones estimate that the risk falls to 1.0 within five years, with significant decreases after two years.

The risk of stroke for a smoker under age 55, according to one broad analysis, is 2.9 times that of a nonsmoker. After quitting, arteriosclerosis is unlikely to be reversed, but it stops increasing so fast, and the numerous effects on the blood brought on by nicotine—on hemoglobin, hematocrit, viscosity, and red blood cell volume—revert rapidly to normal. Blood pressure goes down and more oxygen reaches the brain.

❖ ❖

AN EARLY GRAVE: Robert Louis Stevenson, an inveterate smoker whose life was blighted by tuberculosis, died of a stroke at age 44.

| D A Y   1 3 6 | The job of remaining a non-smoker changes as the days of

being one pile up behind you. At first, it might have been the chief thing going on in your life. Now it's something you have to keep an eye on, but not something you have to think about constantly.

You could still suddenly lose your nonsmoker status. A remarkable number of people who were proud and happy to have quit go back to smoking after many months, or even years, of abstinence. Without quite knowing how, there they are once again, human chimneys, surprised by how much the price of cigarettes has gone up.

How does such a dismal thing happen? Very simply—by smoking one cigarette. As vigilance recedes, the hope that one cigarette won't hurt grows. And then an occasion arises when the sensible mind is taking a nap, and the hand reaches out for a cigarette.

As anybody's brain is going to nap now and then, the hand has to be trained. You must have the conviction that no matter what, you will not reach for a cigarette. You might as well reach for a gun. You don't smoke. Ever. Never.

❖ ❖

"I quit for six months in 1983. Then my dad died and I started smoking again. I've tried to stop again two or three times since but haven't been able to. It's not what my dad would have wanted."

—ELAINE J.

Sandra C. had a nice run of not smoking, lasting through an

```
D A Y   1 3 7
```

upsetting period during which she lost her job and apartment, slept on friends' couches for three months, and finally landed a new job and apartment. In her new job, she manages an apartment complex, so she naturally attended the July Fourth party, where she picked up the smoking habit again. Why?

"I don't know. We were drinking and a bunch of women stayed late, the smokers. So smoking was a social thing to do. I was a little tipsy and we danced and drank and jumped in the pool.

"When I quit again I'll be on my guard. I'll prepare myself in advance so I won't be surprised by my weakness. I could just as well have not smoked."

Sandra has an old story here. Drink has been the undoing of many good intentions. It seems extreme to suggest that a recent ex-smoker should either not drink or should skip the parties, but a return to smoking is a high price to pay for an evening's fun.

❖ ❖

"I often think that somebody should wheel my mother-in-law around to schools as an example of why not to smoke. Nobody was hipper or cooler than she was in her day. Now at age 62 she has emphysema, she can't walk, and she looks 82."

—VICKI T.

| D A Y   1 3 8 | There's more yet to be said about the coronary problems

of smokers. One way you can have a heart attack is through spasms, which is when the muscles around arteries constrict. This can decrease or cut off the blood supply to the heart. Smoking is one cause of these spasms.

Spasms also lead to angina pectoris, which is a result of an inadequate blood supply to the heart. Some people have angina only from exertion, but coronary artery spasms can induce angina at any time. Not only are these attacks painful, they signal high risk for heart attacks. Smokers have a twentyfold risk of vasospastic angina pectoris.

The cheery part of all this is that the risk of death from heart disease drops by half within the first year of stopping smoking. Although it's debatable whether atherosclerosis can be reversed, your blood supply becomes immediately healthier. Right now, your oxygen supply is restored, your platelets are livelier, and your cholesterol has gone down. And if you do have a heart attack, your chance of survival is much better than if you still smoked.

❖ ❖

"At the age of 42, two years after I gave up smoking, I had a massive heart attack. My doctor said if I had been still smoking, it would have killed me."

—MICHAEL TAYLOR, *newspaper reporter, ex-smoker*

It's well known that smokers suffer temptation when trouble be-

falls them. Less expected is the burden that happiness can bring. Smokers have a strange desire to top off good news or good times with a cigarette. It's a temptation that defies explanation, but it's all too familiar to many smokers. Perhaps happiness unleashed is too great to bear? Too unfamiliar? A temptation of fate? For whatever reason, most recent ex-smokers are familiar with the sharp craving for a cigarette that follows quickly on the heels of joy.

And of course you know that the craving will quickly pass, especially if you don't smoke. If you do smoke, the leap of joy will be contained, and you may never find out what happiness you are capable of enduring.

❖   ❖

"I have seen literally thousands of patients who invariably tell me that they feel more energetic, healthy, and alive after they quit [smoking]. But many will also say, as an afterthought, that they are better off in the bedroom. And that you don't know the difference until you quit smoking."
—DR. ALTON OCHSNER

Contrary to myth, more women than men die of heart disease. Relatively protected until menopause, heart disease rates zoom upward among women afterward. While estrogen replacement reduces the risk of heart disease, not smoking is the number-one preventive.

"Smoking is far and away the most important risk factor. Nothing else comes close," says Dr. Robert D. Langer of the University of California at San Diego.

In a British study of women, ever-smokers (with a mean of 25 pack years) were found twice as likely as never-smokers to have suffered heart attacks. A recent American study found current female smokers to have increased their risk of heart attack by 3.7 times. For ex-smokers, the risk was 1.4, although considerably higher (2.6) for women who had stopped smoking only within the previous two years.

FATAL CURVE: In the United States, 250,000 women a year will die of heart attacks, and another 250,000 die of related coronary problems. A woman who has a heart attack is twice as likely to die from it as a man, and if she doesn't die, she's twice as likely to have another attack.

Smokers don't just burn up their homes and kill innocents by smoking in bed. They also toss their cigarette butts out car windows and start forest fires and set their own cars on fire when the butt blows back in the window.

In all, smokers cause more than 200,000 fires with over 1,000 injuries each year. The terrible fire at the Triangle Shirt Waist factory in New York City, which killed 145 young women, was started by a carelessly tossed cigarette butt. Mrs. O'Leary's cow did not start the great Chicago Fire of 1906. It was started by men smoking in the O'Leary barn.

Even if you extinguished every cigarette with the greatest of care when you were a smoker, it is reassuring to think that you are entirely out of the category of persons who inadvertently could be responsible, through smoking, for sparking a terrible disaster.

❖ ❖

FACT: If you count the loss of productivity brought on by smoking diseases, smoking costs every U.S. citizen $221 a year.

| D A Y   1 4 2 | Many smokers suffer from chronic bronchitis, which re-

sults from inflammation in the bronchial tubes. Chronic bronchitis is defined as a recurrent cough or steady sputum production that lasts for at least three months a year. Pneumonia may develop—or worse, chronic obstructive bronchitis, in which the bronchial tubes have become narrowed.

For those with chronic bronchitis, stopping smoking brings a dramatic reduction in inflammation of the bronchial tubes within a month. In two months, smokers' coughs are 100 percent gone. For those with chronic obstructive bronchitis, it is just as important to stop smoking.

"Smoking when your lungs are obstructed is like continuing to run on a sprained ankle," says Dr. Michael Stulbarg, a pulmonary specialist at the University of California at San Francisco. "Every time you smoke a cigarette you are compromising your heart's ability to get oxygen. When you stop, the irritation is immediately lessened, and the cough and sputum production go away. Even the narrowing of the bronchial tubes is partly reversible for people who quit smoking.

"It's hard to bronchoscope smokers because their coughing is so severe," he adds. "I try not to make smokers feel guilty, but they should understand what a difference stopping makes."

A SMOKER'S LIFE: While the average smoker loses eight years of his natural life span, those who succumb to smokers' diseases lose 15 years.

If you still think of cigarettes with longing, try missionary

work. Find a smoker and tell him or her all the reasons you're glad you've quit. Whether you impress the other person or not, you will confirm your own identity as a nonsmoker. Taking action for a cause has the effect of making people feel more strongly about that cause.

By quitting, you've already joined the movement to create a smoke-free nation by the year 2000. You might now take the next step and send in $15 to subscribe to the ASH newsletter (2013 H Street NW, Washington, DC 20006). ASH stands for Action on Smoking and Health and is the largest nationwide organization against smoking; besides publicizing the dangers of smoking, it works through legal channels to protect the public from tobacco.

❖ ❖

"I assure you that the U.S. Public Health Service and its surgeon general—I and whoever comes after me—will do whatever we can to make the dream of a smoke-free society come true."
—C. Everett Koop, M.D.,
Foreword to Merchants of Death *by Larry C. White, 1988*

| D A Y   1 4 4 | While most vascular problems affecting the arms and legs fall

disproportionately on smokers, Burger's disease belongs to them exclusively. Burger's disease (thromboangiitis obliterans) involves the small and medium-size arteries and veins, which become inflamed. There's a severe decrease in blood flow and pressure to the affected fingers, toes, and feet. The sufferer may feel coolness, tingling, and numbness in the early stages. Persistent pain accompanies the more advanced stages. Gangrene and amputation lie at the end of the road.

The only effective treatment is to stop smoking. Otherwise, in the acute stage, progression is unremitting. Astonishingly enough, there are people who cling to their cigarettes right through the numbness and pain and even after being dispossessed of their extremities.

❖ ❖

"Unremitting progression of the acute stage invariably occurs in the patient [with Burger's disease] who continues to smoke and may produce so much tissue damage that amputation is required."

—**The Merck Manual**

"I smoked a lot because I was angry," says one ex-smoker.

"Smoking masked the anger. When I was really mad I'd smoke furiously, feeling that I was getting my revenge, but of course it was myself I was hurting. When I quit, I found out how angry I really was." And what then did she do? "Therapy," she cheerfully admits. She is not an angry person today. Nor does she any longer wish to smoke.

Smoking and anger are frequent mates. The smoking angry person is often remarkably successful in appearing nonchalant and composed. But replacing any kind of action—whether direct or self-calming—with smoking keeps a vicious cycle going. The angrier one gets the more one smokes, and the more one smokes, the less one does about being angry. Besides being self-destructive, an occasional angry smoker indulges in quietly vicious behavior. Most of us would rather deal with someone who knows he's angry than an angry person who thinks he isn't one.

❖ ❖

"The use of healthy all-purpose coping strategies such as self-reinforcement, assertive behavior, social support, relaxation, and exercise has proven important to success in maintaining abstinence in some studies."
—"The Health Benefits of Smoking Cessation," The Surgeon General's Report, *1990*

Smoking spread to Asia in the late sixteenth century, and new users quickly became addicts. Many of the rulers objected to the habit. Tobacco was not sanctioned by the Koran, and it was banned in most Moslem countries. Murad IV of Turkey, who reigned from 1623 to 1640, took a particularly hard line against smokers and had several beheaded. In 1617, Jahangir, the Mogul emperor of Hindustan, ordered that smokers should have their lips slit. The Russian czar Mikhail Feodorovich opted instead for the slitting of the noses—for first offenders. Habitual smokers were to be put to death.

In China, orders went out in 1638 that those who trafficked in tobacco should be decapitated. In Japan after 1606, the shoguns put forth an increasingly severe series of edicts regarding smoking. The later ones mandated jail and loss of property for smokers. Some of these edicts remained in effect until the eighteenth century.

❖ ❖

"As the smoking of tobacco has taken very bad effect upon the health and mind of many persons, I ordered that no one should practice the habit."
—SHAH ABBAS OF PERSIA (reigned 1587–1629)

Psychologists rate people on "self-efficacy," which is the

ability to behave as planned under stress. Not surprisingly, successful quitters score much more highly on self-efficacy than either smokers or failed quitters. While it is likely that the successful quitters have higher self-efficacy than smokers in the first place, there is plenty of anecdotal evidence that quitting in itself raises the score. Obviously, a high sense of self-efficacy would be misplaced in someone who is enslaved to cigarettes.

A slightly different measure, "locus of control," refers to how much someone feels he or she can control personal circumstances. Former smokers show more internal control orientation than failed quitters or ongoing smokers. One study showed no increase in personal control in short-term ex-smokers (less than three months) but large strides for those who had not smoked for longer periods. In measurements of how much control people feel they have over sickness and health, quitters regularly outrate the smokers.

❖ ❖

"It's a big relief to be rid of that sense of guilt I used to have every time I lit a cigarette, thinking, 'I shouldn't be doing this.' "

—JACQUETTA NISBET, *ex-smoker*

Nicotine is defined in the *American Heritage Dictionary* as "a poisonous alkaloid, derived from the tobacco plant, used in medicine and as an insecticide." Tobacco doesn't have to be burned to be toxic. Nicotine can be absorbed through the skin, and new workers in tobacco fields commonly suffer from nausea, dizziness, headaches, vomiting, and other symptoms. With extended exposure, tolerance sets in, and the ill effects become less obvious. Federal health officials recommend that all tobacco harvesters wear protective clothing.

The manufacturing of tobacco products also has been historically a sickening line of work. In 1828, Mr. J. P. Pointe wrote a treatise on the diseases rampant among the workers at the tobacco factory in Lyon, France. Most had respiratory ailments, but they also suffered from gastroenteritis, dysentery, rheumatism, and infections. With automation, workers today are not as freely poisoned, but most of us would still not be anxious to seek jobs in either tobacco fields or factories.

❖ ❖

"Who would have believed that the use of tobacco . . . would have become the vice and custom of almost all the nations of the world; and that so humble a plant, of which the Europeans wrote and spoke so unfavourably, would have made one of the greatest revenues of the kingdoms of Europe?"
—FRANCISCO JAVIER CLAVIJERO,
The History of Mexico, 1618

Now that so many people have become wary of ciga-

rettes, the tobacco industry is promoting snuff and chewing tobacco. Young people in particular are getting the nicotine habit through smokeless tobacco. Because there's no smoke, they think it's safe.

It is not safe. Smokeless tobacco produces an even higher level of nicotine in the bloodstream than cigarettes. Thus, just as with cigarettes, the user is at high risk for heart disease and certain cancers. Smokeless products also create horrible gum problems, erosion and loss of teeth, mouth sores, and oral cancers.

❖ ❖

"I'd like to have the tobacco industry explain a couple of things about the business of chewing tobacco and dipping snuff. Something like 10% to 15% of oral cancers in this country are directly related to snuff dipping. . . . Recent data, for example, from our institute show that snuff dipping among populations in the South . . . is associated with such a very high incidence of cancers of the oral cavity and mouth. . . . We do have cancer mortality maps and the spots stand out on the map so brightly that we had to go down there and find out what was going on. . . . We found out that it was due to snuff dipping."

—DR. VINCENT DEVITA,
Director of the National Cancer Institute,
quoted in Merchants of Death
by Larry C. White, 1988

Personality-wise, smokers are frequently cast out of a different mold than nonsmokers. Casual observation makes this point; so do numerous studies. The smokers are more risk-taking, more impulsive, more unstable, more sex-driven, and more antisocial. Often they're more aggressive and more success-oriented. (Naturally there are plenty of exceptions to the rule.)

Most notably, smokers are more extroverted. Introverts are unlikely to be smokers unless they're chronically depressed.

You may at this point be saying, "Well, then, what is a fun, extroverted, nonconformist like myself doing as a nonsmoker?" Well. Aside from the fact that a lot of extroverts have become nonsmokers lately, there are a few things you may not know about extroverts. Contrary to the general perception of introverts as less feeling, introverts actually react more strongly to stimuli. Consequently, they don't need extra stimuli. Extroverts, on the other hand, suffer from what psychologist H. J. Eysenck calls "stimulus hunger." You might say they're thicker, and stimuli don't penetrate so easily. So they go looking for more. Cigarettes stimulate.

So being an introvert isn't actually so dull. Nor do the other general characteristics of smokers befit a mature, deep-thinking individual. Be glad you've left their ranks.

❖ ❖

For The Record: Eighty percent of schizophrenics are smokers.

Although at one time a lot of high achievers used to be smokers, not many still are. In fact, one of the characteristics that make up the current smoker's profile is downward mobility.

Of the entering class at Harvard, only 2 percent now smoke. Smokers were never at the top of their classes. In 1925, Will H. Brown pointed out in *Tobacco Under the Searchlight* that smoking proliferated at the bottom of the scholarship heap at Yale: in the top third, 25 percent of the students smoked; in the middle third, 41 percent smoked; in the bottom third, 82 percent smoked. Furthermore, he went on to say, the winning crew teams of neither Harvard nor Yale harbored smokers.

It remains the case that few top scholars smoke. Top athletes may have many bad habits, but smoking isn't likely to be one of them. The Olympics are now smoke free.

❖ ❖

"It is idle to distinguish between moderation and excess. The evil is in the thing itself. There is no temperance or rightful moderation in error or vice. There is no lawful indulgence in a bad habit. Temperance requires entire abstinence from things hurtful. Every use of poisons in health is an abuse."
—HENRY GIBBONS, M.D., Tobacco and Its Effects, 1868

People tend to rationalize smoking by those with miserable jobs and sorry lives, saying "What other pleasures do they have?" This point of view was demolished by James Parton back in 1868.

Parton examined the hod carrier, the person who lugged coal and bricks on his shoulders. "No one enjoys the respite of a smoke more than the hod-carrier . . . Does it pay him? I am compelled reluctantly to conclude that it does not." Not only was it bad for his health, said Parton, but "the very fact that it tends to make him contented with his lot is a point against his pipe. . . . a lot which it is his chief and immediate duty to alleviate."

Parton also discussed the soldier, a character universally considered to have the right to smoke. A bad idea, said Parton. Not only does the man in the trenches need to be in peak physical condition and have control of his nerves, "Men were shot during the war [Civil War] merely because they would strike a light and smoke." In modern wars, men have continued to be killed for the same reason.

❖ ❖

When visiting the homes of the poor: "Better the merry son, the cheerful talk, the pleasant stroll, than this dulling of the sense and the brain in smoke."

—JAMES PARTON,
Does It Pay to Smoke and Drink? *1868*

The greatest changes that come from giving up smoking

are not always measurable, or even easy to describe.

"So much has changed in the twelve years since I stopped smoking that it's hard to pinpoint which ones are the rewards of not smoking. But there's one thing that I do credit to my escape from cigarettes, and that's a capacity for joy, which crept up on me just a few years ago.

"The first time was at a concert of the Berlioz Requiem. I was just overjoyed all through it and had few conscious thoughts.

"A few other times since then I've been swimming with happiness as I never did before. I always used to be more of a depressive. I can't say I'm always jolly now, and I don't really want to be, but knowing that I've had these moments puts value on my life. It's a balance on the scale for all the trouble life puts one through."

❖ ❖

"I am perfectly sure that I would never have found this capacity for joy if I still smoked. Smoking drags you down, smoking interferes, smoking replaces feeling. It takes a long time to replace smoking, but I've gotten more out of not smoking than I expected. I was going to be satisfied with not getting extra wrinkles or cancer."

—SYLVIA T., *ex-smoker*

```
D A Y   1 5 4
```
In the past, health plans didn't identify smokers, and there was little data about smokers' medical expenses. The figures are now coming in. A recent study published in the *Journal of Occupational Medicine* analyzed the paid claims of a large group plan over an eleven-month period.

Tobacco users had 124 hospital admissions per thousand; nonusers had 76 per thousand. Once in the hospital, tobacco users stayed longer—6.47 days versus the nonuser's 5.03 days. The average insurance payment to a smoker was $1,145; to a nonsmoker it was only $762.

Nonsmokers are heavily subsidizing smokers—with insurance payments, with taxes, and with little hidden outlays, such as maintaining fire departments. And that's just the financial cost. The cost in heartbreak and suffering is worse. If the younger generation now starting smoking continues to smoke, the price will be vast.

❖ ❖

GOOD MEDICINE: *The doctors at one large health care network estimated that if all their patients stopped smoking it would do more good than all the health care of every kind that they could possibly deliver.*

Adolescents are the fastest growing group of new smok-

ers. If history repeats itself, 90 percent of those who smoke even three or four cigarettes will go on to smoke for thirty or forty years.

Our best-adjusted adolescents are not the ones getting hooked. Those who take up smoking are apt to be the lonely children, the ones who dislike school and who have no future plans, and those who have low opinions of themselves.

The strongest influences on adolescents regarding smoking are their parents and their peer groups. Interestingly, it has sometimes been found that parents' attitudes toward smoking have more influence than parents' behavior. So even smoking parents can influence their children not to smoke if they rail against the habit and emphasize their own regrets that they ever acquired it.

As a nonsmoker, you can now present both a good example and a personal witness against smoking to any children you might be around. And you can be thankful that in quitting smoking you finally have evidence of having recovered from your own adolescent problems.

❖ ❖

"I started smoking because my mother smoked. I wanted to be able to say, 'Boy, I really need a cigarette.' I wanted to be addicted."

—DANIEL L., *21-year-old smoker*

One would expect women's magazines to be regularly delivering to their readers all the news regarding women and smoking. They are not. To find out why not, one need only thumb through the cigarette advertising. There are a few exceptions, but in most the cigarette ads are prominent. Some magazines are dependent on tobacco advertising for their survival and do not wish to risk losing these ads.

Consequently, despite a constant dose of health articles, the manifold dangers inherent in smoking do not get top billing. Generally, outright censorship isn't necessary. The editorial board simply understands that hard-hitting articles about tobacco could bring trouble from advertisers. So why not write hard-hitting articles about some substance that doesn't advertise? So the full horror story about smoking and premature babies, cervical cancer, osteoporosis, wrinkles, and other effects is left on the shelf.

❖ ❖

YOU'VE COME THE WRONG WAY, BABY: *An analysis of 1,462 women between the ages of 38 and 60 in Gothenburg, Sweden, found the smokers with significantly fewer teeth. A follow-up study twelve years later discovered that the smokers had in the intervening years lost 67 percent more teeth. These statistics proved independent of socioeconomic level, education, and brushing and flossing.*

"Costa Mesa, California— Wayne McLaren, who por-

trayed the rugged Marlboro Man in cigarette ads but became an anti-smoking crusader after developing lung cancer, died Wednesday at the age of 51.

"Mr. McLaren, who smoked for about 25 years, learned he had the disease about two years ago. Last spring, he appeared before a meeting of stockholders of Philip Morris Inc., maker of Marlboro, and asked them to limit their advertising. He also made public appearances to warn about the dangers of smoking.

"Mr. McLaren, a rodeo rider, actor and Hollywood stuntman, was one of several dozen models hired in 1975 to appear in Marlboro magazine and billboard ads, evoking a tough and handsome image for the brand. He was a pack-and-a-half-a-day smoker for about 25 years, he once said.

"Chemotherapy and radiation treatment appeared to successfully kill the cancer, but it was learned in January that the cancer had spread to Mr. McLaren's brain."

—© *San Francisco Chronicle*, July 24, 1991,
reprinted by permission

❖   ❖

Just For The Record: Mr. McLaren smoked Kools, not Marlboros.

`D A Y   1 5 8` Bladder cancer is an excellent reason not to go back to smoking today or ever. Studies have repeatedly shown a strong link between smoking and bladder cancer, and cigarette smoke includes naphtylamine, a known urinary carcinogen. Conclusions as to degree of risk vary, but most investigations have found smokers with three to four times the rate of bladder cancer of never-smokers. On average, quitters carry twice the risk of those who have never smoked; the risk is directly related to the amount smoked and the length of the smoking career. Under all circumstances, men run higher odds than women.

Unlike the risk of heart disease, your risk for bladder cancer does not plummet with your last cigarette, but one study did show it halving after six years. Yet it may take twenty years for an ex-smoker's risk to fall to that of a never-smoker. Thus, if you are 98 years old, worry about bladder cancer is probably not your best reason for not smoking, but for the rest of you, bladder cancer is nothing to fool around with. For anyone diagnosed with bladder cancer, it is particularly important to quit because of the high recurrence rate among those who continue smoking.

HINC ILLAE LACRIMAE (THUS THESE TEARS): *Hubert Humphrey, former United States vice president and a smoker until age 17, died of bladder cancer at age 67.*

Filters made cigarettes more palatable to a lot of people,

but they haven't done much to save lives. On the contrary. People who had resisted getting shreds of tobacco in their mouths became smokers—and died of the habit.

The idea of the filter is to reduce the amount of nicotine and tar sucked in. And indeed, when a cigarette is hooked up to a smoking machine, which usually inhales twice a minute, the filter is effective. But give a nicotine addict a low-nicotine cigarette and she'll smoke more cigarettes, take deeper drags, puff more often, and smoke the cigarette right down to the filter. These techniques enable her to get just as much nicotine and tar as she did from her old, high-poison brand. What's more, by inhaling more she's increasing her dose of the gases in tobacco smoke that aren't slowed by filters.

If a low-tar, high-nicotine cigarette could be made it might possibly reduce cancer rates, but it's fairly pointless to smoke cigarettes and try to block nicotine. The nicotine is the reason to smoke. Herbal cigarettes will never become popular.

❖ ❖

FACT: Filters do nothing for the sidestream smoker, who would be better off if the smoker smoked stronger cigarettes but fewer of them.

Suppose you have stopped smoking but your mate or some other member of your household has not. You are at higher risk for relapse than someone inhabiting a more wholesome atmosphere.

However, it would not be reasonable for you to turn on your spouse with any great reforming vigor. As you chose your own time to quit, so does your mate deserve to choose his or hers. What's more, nagging is more apt to lead to defiance than to compliance. It's enough to offer your shining example, coupled with only an iota of silent disapproval.

What is reasonable is to expect your significant other to practice his/her habit somewhere that you aren't. An ex-smoker shouldn't have to inhabit a smoke-filled living room or bedroom. Many spouses have set up little nooks for themselves in garages, basements, or porches. The sight of the poor smoker shivering, pelted by rain, or exposed to summer heat is helpful too in dimming your memories of the joys of smoking.

❖ ❖

"Because my husband had asthma, for the last five years of my smoking, I smoked on the porch. So that made quitting easier as most of the things I did weren't associated with smoking. I did miss the cigarette I had with my morning tea on the porch so I gave up drinking tea. Now, because we're both retired, I don't get up until I'm ready so I don't need a stimulant."

—MICKY GRAESER, *ex-smoker*

Smoking affects human cells on the most basic level. A 1990 study of tissues taken at autopsy—of both smokers and nonsmokers—gave evidence of excessive changes in the DNA in smokers, particularly in tissues from the lungs, bladder, and pancreas. The degree of damage in the lungs was particularly significant. Another 1990 study examined DNA from smokers' bladder and lungs, finding evidence of damage in both, which was less extreme in the ex-smokers than in the lifelong smokers.

❖   ❖

TOBACCO POWER: The United States tobacco industry leads all other industries in profitability. Tobacco companies have avoided obvious price-fixing, but prices have risen regularly, fast outpacing the consumer price index. Cigarette taxes, on the other hand, have proportionally decreased. In 1955, taxes constituted almost half the price of cigarettes; today they are only one-quarter.

While Americans were quitting smoking throughout the eighties, the tobacco companies enjoyed rising profits; the defection of a proportion of the smokers was compensated by other smokers who smoked more. Consequently, per capita consumption did not fall greatly; meanwhile, thanks to cheap imported tobacco, the price of the raw materials was going down. Cheap cigarettes are now threatening profits, but tobacco companies plan to make up the difference with sales abroad.

Tolstoy felt that far too little attention was paid to tobacco as
an intoxicant. Because tobacco is taken in small regular doses,
smokers do not act as demented as people under the influence
of alcohol. But still, Tolstoy felt, even the mild intoxication of tobacco leads to shameful behavior.

❖ ❖

*"Every smoker may observe in himself this definite necessity
for intoxicating himself with tobacco at certain difficult
moments. I remember when it was during the period
of my smoking that I used to feel a special necessity for
tobacco. This was always in such minutes when I was anxious
not to remember what I did remember, when I wanted to
forget, not to think. I am sitting alone, doing nothing,
and I know that I must begin to work, but I do not feel
like working. I smoke a cigarette, and continue to sit. I
promised somebody to call on him at five o'clock, and I have
stayed too long in another place; I recall that I am late,
but I do not want to think of it—so I smoke. I am excited
and I tell a man a lot of disagreeable things, and I know
that I am doing wrong, and I see that it is time to stop,
but I . . . smoke and continue to excite myself."*
    —LEO TOLSTOY, Why People Become Intoxicated, *1890*

There are a few ex-smokers who claim no great benefits

from giving up cigarettes. "I don't feel physically any different," says Doris Ober, a writer who gave up a two-pack-a-day habit. "I don't have more energy, and my taste buds aren't perkier.

"I quit five years ago because I finally bought the health message, but all I've gotten out of it is the peace of mind that I'm not poisoning other people or harming myself."

For Ober, this is enough. She walks a mile a day with only the same ease she had when she smoked. She didn't gain a sense of mastery from quitting because she always believed she could stop if she wanted to, although she was a smoker who loved to smoke.

The best part, says Doris, was that she found she could still write. "I was very, very fearful that if I couldn't light a cigarette when I sat down at my desk the whole flow would be cut off. I was happy to find that that didn't happen." This may be faint praise, but other writers have died for their false beliefs in smoking.

❖ ❖

CHEMICAL WARFARE: A few of the toxins inhaled in tobacco: cyanide, formaldehyde, methanol, acetylene, naphtylamine, ammonia, nitrogen oxide, carbon monoxide. And nicotine.

| D A Y   1 6 4 |

Helen Whitney smoked from age 15 to age 39. Five years before she quit she married a nonsmoker, and she gives him tremendous credit for having never nagged her. "You know you should stop anyhow, and if someone nags, you feel that you're doing something wrong all the time. It doesn't help.

"But I realized that my smoking was an inconvenience to my husband as well as to me. I'd always wanted to stop, but I never thought I had the willpower. I reduced my smoking and told myself every day that I had to stop, but added that it would have to be easy or I wouldn't be able to.

"And then one day I stopped, and it was easy. I was ready. I did what I could to make it easier. I gave up tea because that went with cigarettes, and as soon as a meal was over, I jumped up and cleared the table. In fact, that got to be a habit and I still do it. I haven't had a desire to smoke since."

❖　❖

Going Nowhere: A study of youths 17 to 18 years of age found that 43 percent of the dropouts smoked versus 17 percent of those who were attending or had graduated from high school.

Certain studies have shown

that nicotine actually does help people perform some tasks on tests. But George Spilich, a psychologist, disputes the conclusion that smoking is an aid to thinking. His tests showed that nicotine improved performance only on the simplest tasks. On harder tests, the smokers' scores went down. For story recollection and for detecting the main point of an article, nonsmokers outperformed smokers.

In driving simulation, the smokers drove slightly farther in the allotted time than the nonsmokers—but had three times as many accidents.

Dianna Holden and Elizabeth Driscoll compared the short-term memories of smoking and nonsmoking college students. In their test, the students were given a set of items to remember. The smokers smoked just before taking the test. The nonsmokers scored higher, and their reaction times were faster.

Holden and Driscoll theorize that the smokers' performance is affected by the lower levels of oxygen in their blood. They conclude, "Our evidence does not support the common smoker's statement that it helps me think and concentrate."

❖　❖

"People generally say, and I used to say, that smoking contributes to mental work. This is unquestionably so, if one considers the amount of mental work. A smoker, who therefore has ceased to value strictly or to weigh his thoughts, imagines that a mass of ideas has suddenly come to him. But this does not mean at all that he has acquired a mass of thoughts, but only that he has lost control over his thoughts ... there will be more work, but its quality is lowered."
—LEO TOLSTOY, Why People Become Intoxicated, 1890

Smokers with high blood pressure don't get much benefit from medical treatment. An analysis of five separate studies of patients taking medication showed the smokers dying at twice the rate of the nonsmokers. In one of the studies, the nonsmokers in the placebo group suffered fewer complications than smokers under active treatment. Smokers with both high blood pressure and high cholesterol levels had particularly poor prospects, dying at ten times the rate of hypertensive nonsmokers with lower cholesterol. Beta-blockers helped the nonsmokers but had no effect on the coronary death rates of smokers.

The moral is obviously that if you have high blood pressure, smoking is not an option for you. You probably quit in the nick of time.

❖   ❖

"An experiment on patients with heart failure measured their heart and vascular performance after they had smoked just two cigarettes. The conclusion: 'Smoking elicits significant hemodynamic effects in patients with congestive heart failure, many unfavorable and potentially detrimental.'"

—**American Journal of Medical Sciences,** *1989*

Some smokers have a habit consisting of one to five ciga-

rettes a day. Most of us ex-pack and carton smokers look at this as a habit so piddling it hardly bears mention. But these people suffer too when the time comes to quit. The following are the testimonies of minimal smokers who quit:

"I never bought cigarettes, just bummed one or two a day. I didn't think it hurt me until I took up lap-swimming, when I kept having to stop and cling to the side of the pool to catch my breath. I quit smoking, which was surprisingly hard, and in a few weeks I could swim for a half-hour without stopping." (Michael Lipsey)

"I smoked three to five cigarettes a day at specific times . . . I never even thought of myself as a smoker, but I missed my cigarettes badly when I gave them up. I only quit so that I could lecture my friends about smoking, but now I think I was slightly asthmatic and never should have smoked at all. My lungs are much clearer." (Vicki Lindner)

"I used to smoke an occasional cigarette, but I don't any more. I wouldn't ever want my daughter to see me smoking, and my husband would find it repellent. The idea of smoking still has some glamour for me, but not in the logical part of my mind." (Meryl Larsen)

FACT: One cigarette raises the blood pressure and pulse, makes platelets stickier, lowers circulation, and sticks tar in the lungs.

Cigarettes are the leading cause of death by fire. Smoking caused 33,400 home fires in 1989, in which 1,050 people died and 2,855 more were injured. A carelessly discarded cigarette set off 76 percent of these fires, and in 12 percent of them someone fell asleep while smoking.

The majority of the people hurt were asleep when the fire started. The National Fire Protection Association (NFPA), which collects these figures, estimates that 18 percent of the victims were impaired by drugs or alcohol, a figure that may be understated. For one thing, confides the NFPA, "it is very difficult for fire officials to assess the prior condition of a fatal victim."

Many innocents, often children, die in fires started by somebody's cigarette. Old people are at high risk of being that somebody—the combination of age impairment and smoking can be deadly. Most smokers think, "I wouldn't do that," but the majority of smokers who have started fires were not impaired or bedridden or drunk. A moment's carelessness is all it takes. Anybody can start a fire.

❖   ❖

The Brighter Side: The number of residential home fires caused annually by cigarettes has declined along with the U.S. smoking rate.

"Sometimes I can't imagine why I don't take a cigarette,"

says Carol A., age 46, who stopped smoking two yeas ago. "At my brother's funeral, which nobody showed up for, I desperately wanted to smoke. I honestly don't think it's a question of will. My will is telling me to smoke, but my spirit says no."

Carol first quit many years ago and then started having the occasional cigarette with friends. "Slowly and surely, it kind of escalated," she says. "It was terribly difficult to stop again, but I was embarrassed to be smoking. Although in a funny way I liked the unfashionable part of it. When you smoke these days you meet such nice people. They're the walking wounded. But it was depressing too, and I was short of breath almost instantly and coughing terribly in the morning. So I sort of offered up my cigarettes in my meditation practice, and I did stop. Every once in a while I have the urge, but obviously I'm not someone who can smoke just one cigarette. At heart I'm a smoker."

❖ ❖

". . . the modern cigarette is a highly efficient device for getting nicotine to the brain. The smoke is mild enough to be inhaled deeply into the alveoli of the lungs from where nicotine is rapidly absorbed into the bloodstream to reach the brain within about 7 seconds. This means that the inhaling cigarette smoker receives a rapid intravenous-like 'shot' or bolus of nicotine to the brain after each inhaled puff."

—M. A. H. RUSSELL AND M. J. JARVIS,
Pharmacological Adjuncts in Smoking Cessation,
NIDA Research Monograph #53, 1985

Not so long ago, a nonsmoker married to a smoker was considered a fussy nag if he or she complained overly about the smoke. Thanks to a great deal of research, the tide has turned. Passive smoking has been elevated to number three on the list of preventable causes of death, following active smoking and drinking. Now someone who tolerates a spouse smoking in the living quarters can reasonably be considered a doormat.

People exposed to cigarette smoke show significant reductions in lung capacity. The risk for lung cancer goes up 30 percent to 100 percent for husbands and wives of smokers. Nonsmoking wives of smokers have a risk of Chronic Obstructive Pulmonary Disease 80 percent greater than those married to nonsmokers.

The evidence is piling up also on the subject of heart disease. Blood tests of people exposed to cigarette smoke show stickier platelets (a risk for blood clots) and increased cholesterol. A Chinese study concluded that nonsmoking women married to smokers tripled their odds of coronary heart disease. Most estimates are more moderate than this; a study of wives from Evans County, Georgia, came up with an elevated risk of 1.59. The degree of risk depends greatly on such variables as how much the spouse smokes at home and how ventilated the house is.

❖ ❖

DEATH BE NOT PROUD: *Passive smoking is credited with 53,000 deaths a year.*

Smoke in the workplace may
be even more deadly than

| D A Y   1 7 1 |

smoke at home. At work, people spend even more time shut up
in small spaces with bad ventilation. Also, people who smoke
tend to smoke a lot at work. Whereas a New Zealand study
found the lung cancer risk from passive smoking at home to be
1.3, passive smokers at work clocked in a 2.2 risk.

The risk for ischemic heart disease—too little oxygen reaching the heart—computed out for passive smokers at work at
2.3, compared to 1.3 for passive smoking at home. Besides
higher risks for these and other illnesses, passive smokers rou-
tinely suffer from eye irritation, headaches, nausea, and dizziness.

When people first quit smoking they are apt to still identify
with smokers and thus be tolerant of smoking. But as time goes
by, they increasingly think of clean air as a right. If you're bothered by smoke at work or in public places and want to find out
what to do about it, or just want to help the cause, join Americans for Nonsmokers' Rights (510-841-3032) at 2530 San
Pablo Avenue, Suite J, Berkeley, CA 94702.

*THE CASUALTY LIST: Waitresses have the highest mortality
rate of any predominantly female work force in California,
and secondhand smoke has been identified as the cause.
Their rate of lung cancer is 50 percent to 90 percent
higher than average, even factoring out smoking. Their heart
disease rates are twice the norm. Smoke exposure in restaurants
can be up to five times that of a typical workplace.*

You've probably noticed that there's an extreme range in reactions to quitting smoking. At one end are the people who claim, "It doesn't change anything; I just don't smoke." At the other end are those who say, "I had to change everything in my life."

Part of the difference could be that some people simply aren't introspective. Giving up smoking may have had more impact on their lives than they imagine. However, it is also clear that to some ex-smokers, cigarettes weren't terribly important. Although addicted to nicotine, smoking didn't fill up any big holes in their lives. Once they were over the withdrawal, life went on as before.

To other people, cigarettes were their asylum, and without them life could never be the same. Without cigarettes, they felt tremendous loneliness. Many people agree that they had to become more open in expressing themselves once they no longer had cigarettes around as pacifiers or emotion stuffers. The new mode does not always sit well with the nearest and dearest. Although intimacy is limited with someone whose best friend is a cigarette, there are advantages to having a partner who keeps his or her mouth closed. But need we add, this is no excuse for cigarette suicide?

❖   ❖

THE ODDS: Of one hundred regular smokers, one will be murdered, two will die in traffic accidents, and 25 will be killed by tobacco.

Smoking affects a smoker's blood in numerous ways.

Smokers have white blood cell counts up to 30 percent higher than those of nonsmokers; T-cells, autoantibodies, and immunoglobulins are also affected. The upshot is that smokers' immune systems are inhibited.

Smokers have been shown in many tests to have reduced immune responses. For instance, among poultry workers the nonsmokers produce more antibodies against hen serum antigen than the smokers. In a flu outbreak among 336 military men, 68 percent of the smokers got sick and only 47 percent of the former and never-smokers did.

Children of smokers have an increased risk of a variety of infections—digestive as well as respiratory. Children of smoking parents are three to four times as likely to be hospitalized with serious infectious diseases. The supposition is that passive smoking generally depresses the children's immune systems, giving them less resistance to infections. However, once the household stops smoking, everybody's immune systems return to normal.

❖ ❖

"I see not therefore how tobacco can be acquitted from procuring the overthrow of the perfect state both of body and mind; and that not only in [smokers] themselves, but in their posterity also: for the temperament and constitution of the father is ordinarily transferred into the children ... and the affections of the mind also."
—E.D., "Dr. of Physic," London, 1606

Some occasional smokers kick the habit partly to express disapproval for the cigarette industry. Such intense feelings are widespread, and yet the industry prospers. Tobacco companies have divested their resources, but none are eager to leave the tobacco business altogether; it is the most profitable business in the country. Thus, companies will spend tremendous sums on defending lawsuits, lobbying, and advertising.

However, the profit to the farmer has declined steadily over the years, and from the price of a pack, the grower now gets a mere 5 percent. Nonetheless, the gross per acre remains much higher than for any other crop. Tobacco is grown on small farms, and we might well sympathize with the struggling farmers should all demand for the crop cease. Biosource Genetics Corp. has one answer: a gene expression system that can induce tobacco plants to produce the antiviral therapeutic protein tichosanthin.

❖   ❖

NOT THAT DESPERATE: *"Despite a tight job market, a survey of this year's M.B.A. graduates at 12 schools found that 79 percent would refuse to work for tobacco producers. In 1990, only 61 percent had been so disinclined."*
—**The Wall Street Journal**, *July 22, 1992*

Addicts come in many forms, and by no means are all of

them hooked to illegal drugs. Those hooked to cigarettes find quitting very tough for the same reasons that any other drug addicts are stuck to their drugs.

In *The Addictive Personality*, Craig Nakken analyzes the drive of the addict. Happiness and peace of mind, he says, naturally come and go in cycles that people rarely can control. Addicts are dedicated to controlling the cycles. Through a relationship with an object, the addict keeps up an out-of-control search for wholeness, happiness, and peace of mind.

The object is trusted to produce mood change and emotional fulfillment; the smoke addict is involved in a pathological relationship with cigarettes. "People normally get emotional and intimacy needs met through intimate connections with other people, themselves, their community, and with a spiritual power greater than themselves," writes Nakken. The smoke addict instead looks to cigarettes for nurturance. According to Nakken, "The mood change gives the illusion that a need has been met. . . . Addiction makes life very lonely and isolated." But not hopeless. Tune in tomorrow.

❖   ❖

"My affair with cigarettes has been the greatest passion of my life. I am a nicotine addict."

—FRANK C., *ex-smoker*

| D A Y   1 7 6 | Addiction is a commitment to a negative life-style, which pro-
duces as by-products shame and loss of self-respect. The first
step for people recovering from addiction, according to Craig
Nakken (author of *The Addictive Personality*) is to own up to
having an addictive personality—which means having low impulse control, a controlling personality, and a mistrust of people. The cigarette addict without cigarettes is only at Stage
One of recovery.

"Honesty must be the backbone of one's recovery program," writes Nakken. Recovery, he says, lies in forming
honest and healthy relationships with other people. He recommends getting a start on this in self-help groups.

Readers who see themselves in the profile of the addict de-
scribed here should make every effort to attend Nicotine Anonymous. If, however, Nicotine Anonymous hasn't made it to your
area, you can probably find other twelve-step programs you
could qualify for. Or you can start a group yourself (write Nicotine Anonymous, World Services, 2118 Greenwich Street,
San Francisco, CA 94123).

❖   ❖

*"I have set before you life and death, blessing and cursing.
Choose life."*

—*DEUTERONOMY 30:19*

"I finally quit when it got to me that smoking wasn't something

I was doing because I liked myself," says Bonnie F. "But it took me ten years to get to that point. My reasons for smoking were all mixed up with sophistication, weight control, and rebellion. My parents had been heavy smokers and said I couldn't smoke until I got my first job. This was in Pittsburgh, then a mill town, where only the wild kids smoked.

"So naturally I smoked. In my twenties I tried to quit and couldn't. I didn't have a clue why not." In her thirties, Fox tried acupuncture, hypnosis, and nicotine gum. "I'd quit a while and then go back, saying to myself that life was a mess and I was a nonentity and what did it matter what I did?

"It wasn't until I got hold of my fears that I quit successfully. I was constantly afraid that I just couldn't survive in the world. I also realized that smoking wasn't my only addiction. Addiction was a basic flaw and a symptom of my feelings of inadequacy. At the same time I was having some success in life, and once I became aware of my fears, I had a lot of breakthroughs in my art and in other areas. And I stopped smoking."

❖   ❖

"The positive support for nonsmoking encouraged me—that I couldn't smoke on airplanes or in certain restaurants or in friends' houses. The best solution was quitting."
                                                    —BONNIE F., *ex-smoker*

| D A Y   1 7 8 | "There's a very high relation- |

"There's a very high relationship between smoking and periodontal disease," says Dr. Lary Schiller, a San Francisco periodontist. "And someone with severe problems who continues smoking does not have a very good chance of successful treatment."

The troublemaker is not just direct irritation from the smoke but also the chemistry of nicotine in the bloodstream. Normally, where there's infection, white blood cells congregate at the site and destroy the bacteria, but a smoker's blood vessels are constricted. The capillaries don't open as they should, and white blood cells are inhibited in their rescue mission.

Besides all that, smokers often don't take as good care of their teeth as nonsmokers, presumably because of their general failure to see the cause and effect between what they do and what happens to them. Now that you belong among the nonsmokers, you can revel in proper brushing and flossing.

❖ ❖

THE SMOKER'S LIFE: Smokers not only have stains on their teeth, but their tongues are also heavily coated with tar.

Even now, you may occasionally cast a fond thought in the

direction of your old friend, tobacco. And why not? As with a
lover who rarely showed up on time and beat you when he
did, there were still the good times.

From whence did they come, these good times? Mostly
through your neurotransmitters. The miracle of nicotine is that it
can mimic acetylcholine, which fires off a number of other neurotransmitters: norepinephrine, dopamine, and epinephrine are
just a few. Epinephrine sets the adrenal glands going—heart
rate beating, blood pressure rising, extremities bloodless.
Other neurotransmitters promote a relaxant effect. Large doses
of nicotine may block neurotransmission and sedate the
smoker.

The accomplished smoker can somewhat regulate the effect
by his rate of puffing. But all too often, as with the bad lover,
it just isn't working. You feel lousy. You're worn out. Your nerves
are frayed. And yet you can't let go.

Next time those cigarettes come knocking, whatever you
do, don't let them in.

❖ ❖

*"There is a strong tendency among former users to relapse,
sometimes months or even years after quitting. Cigarette
smokers may experience this to a greater degree than
do users of other drugs."*

—NATIONAL INSTITUTE ON DRUG ABUSE

| D A Y   1 8 0 | Are smokers responsible for their own smoking? Or are
they helpless addicts? This is a major question of law and government policy. The fact that most smokers smoke because they can't quit suggests that the smoker has little control.

But are smokers unwilling victims? One certainly smokes that first cigarette of one's own free will, but most people smoked that one as teenagers, before reaching the age of consent. Eighty-five percent of the teens who then smoke another cigarette become regular smokers.

The surgeon general and nearly all smokers agree that smoking is addictive. Only the tobacco companies prefer to think otherwise. If people are smoking from addiction rather than for pleasure, that leaves tobacco companies in the despised company of drug providers preying on weakness.

And if people are addicts, it then behooves the government to do whatever is possible to discourage smoking. Free will is not at issue.

"What tax-induced price rises might do is make the habit substantially less attractive to teenagers not yet addicted to the drug ... any given price increase is almost six times more likely to make teenagers stop or never start smoking than it would adults."
—ROBERT E. GOODIN,
No Smoking: The Ethical Issues, 1989

Until recently, the opinion in hospitals was that the patients

were suffering enough and should not be asked to add nicotine withdrawal to their afflictions. This opinion has changed. The new thinking is that a patient in the hospital is found at a teachable moment, which should be taken advantage of. Furthermore, considering that most smokers want to quit, some 30 percent of sicknesses are smoking related, smokers are hospitalized more than nonsmokers, and smoking interferes with recovery and contributes to malnutrition, the whole idea of smoking in hospitals seems balmy.

Consequently, the Joint Commission on Accreditation of Hospitals decided that, starting on January 1, 1992, no hospital could be accredited unless it was smoke free. Hospitals have two years to comply. The fact that few doctors still smoke probably made this requirement more palatable.

As a nonsmoker, should you suddenly wake up in the hospital, you will certainly be more comfortable than someone who will be compelled to quit on entry.

❖ ❖

THE CASUALTY LIST: An analysis of the patients during one 24-hour period in the Kansas City Veterans Administration Hospital found 32 percent of them hospitalized with smoking-related diseases. Doubtless a percentage of the rest had conditions exacerbated by smoking.

Having lived now for six months without a cigarette, you can give yourself a rousing cheer and begin to think of yourself as a confirmed nonsmoker. Your chances of not taking up the habit again are good. Your body has adjusted to not smoking, and your moods are likely to have improved. Your self-esteem should be high. After all, you have succeeded where the majority have failed. Fewer than 30 percent of those who quit smoking six months ago are still nonsmokers.

"Giving up smoking was the hardest thing I ever did," says Ann Kidd, who quit twenty years ago. Heroin addicts generally say that giving up heroin is easier than quitting smoking. Most sober alcoholics would testify that foregoing drink was minor league compared to living without cigarettes. Hang on to the memory of what the withdrawal was like for you. If there's danger of the memory fading, sit down and write a letter to yourself, recording your sufferings. Keep the letter within easy reach.

Now that you're on the sunny side of the statistics, your biggest danger is that you might relax your vigilance. Mark Frauenfelder started smoking again after six months of freedom from cigarettes. How could he? "I stopped putting energy into not smoking," he said. "And there I was again, cigarette in hand."

❖ ❖

"We swim in a sea of carcinogens, in which the cigarette is the great white shark."

—WILLIAM G. CAHAN, M.D.

With 50,000-plus studies showing how bad smoking is,

one would expect that smokers would make even more heroic efforts than they do to quit. And yet smokers will fret about plane crashes and snakebites, all the while inhaling a substance that kills 25 percent of its users and to some degree debilitates the rest.

In *Smoking: The Ethical Issues*, Robert Goodin considers that smokers operate under "cognitive defects." Some people simply deny that cigarettes are as dangerous as reports say. "Oh, everything's dangerous," they will comfort themselves. "Pesticides in fruit, hormones in bacon, etc."

Even smokers who acknowledge the perils of smoking are surprisingly ignorant of specifics. One poll found over half of smokers did not know that smoking accounted for most cases of lung cancer, bronchitis, and emphysema.

Then there is the anchoring fallacy: The smoker has smoked cigarettes over and over again and nothing bad has happened. Thus his own experience tells him that smoking is safe. The saddest part is that when the telltale X ray comes back, it's often too late for a new start.

❖ ❖

TEENAGE ADDICTION: About 16 percent of American teenagers (ages 12 to 18) smoke, most under the illusion that they will quit within a year. However, three out of four of those who have attempted to quit have failed.

| D A Y   1 8 4 | "Time discounting" is another cognitive defect that smokers suffer from. If I lose playing at Russian roulette with a six-shooter, I will pay immediately, but the big bill for the cigarette I smoke today won't come due for some years.

It's something like a mortgage with a balloon payment coming up in twenty or thirty years. The early payments are annoying but tolerable—the cough, the shortness of breath, the price of cigarettes—but the balloon payment, when the time comes, is dreadful.

You may even have to move out of your house (your body). Even if not so unlucky as that, the smoking 85-year-old is not liable to be found working out in the garden all day long.

Especially for young smokers, the moment of truth seems too far away to be worth worrying about. And old age hardly seems worth bothering with. But those who have found their ways there discover the value of proper preparation.

❖ ❖

"Let not the smoker or chewer flatter himself that he is sound and secure because he feels no harm. The deadliest maladies often take silent possession of the vital organs without disturbing the general health. Death steals upon us in our sleep."

—HENRY GIBBONS, **Tobacco and Its Effects**, 1868

Although the careful studies de-
ducing risk factors for smoking

are recent, doctors centuries ago spotted the "smoker's heart." Autopsies showed the damage, and even casual observers noted that smokers were less likely to stay the long course of life.

President McKinley died in 1901, having lingered several days after being shot. His doctor claimed that McKinley would have recuperated had he not had a "nicotine heart." (We might note that his assassin was also a nicotine fiend.)

❖ ❖

"The earliest effect is upon the heart ... then upon the general nervous system, including the brain (the latter showing itself in insomnia, loss of memory, and later in want of proper mental control). Finally the nutrition of the entire system suffers."

—CHARLES GATCHELL, M.D.,
quoted in Tobacco: The Cigarette —
Why It Is Especially Objectionable
by Winfield S. Hall, 1900

| D A Y   1 8 6 | Smokers predictably underesti-mate how much they smoke,

and researchers have learned not to take a smoker's cigarette count at face value. Claims of a third less than the actual consumption are the norm. The motivation is much more likely to be wishful thinking than intentional deception.

It's easy for a smoker to kid himself. You just don't count. If you smoke the nine remaining cigarettes in a pack in the morning, open a new pack in the afternoon, and then open another pack the next morning, you can fancy yourself a pack-a-day smoker.

Not that a pack a day is light smoking. It's plenty to qualify for all the major diseases, especially if you keep it up for a couple of decades. Ann Kidd's aunt smoked just a few cigarettes a day; she died of lung cancer. Another woman who appears in this book never inhaled; she has Chronic Obstructive Pulmonary Disease. You never know which cigarette is one too many.

❖ ❖

"We regard a pack a day as heavy smoking."
—MICHAEL STULBARG, M.D.,
Director of Pulmonary Service,
University of California at San Francisco

The tobacco industry has been a big contributor to both politi-

cal parties, with the largest donations going to the Republicans. In return, the Republicans have been good to the tobacco industry. The Reagan and Bush administrations were heavily laden with tobacco advocates, who fought for tobacco exports, resisted smoking bans, and opposed increases in cigarette taxes. The Chairman of the 1992 Republican Convention, Craig Fuller, was a vice president of Philip Morris.

The Clintons promptly banned smoking in the White House upon moving in, and as of this writing, there are other hopeful signs that the Clinton administration is not going to be a boon to the tobacco industry. As governor of Arkansas, Clinton vetoed a smokers' rights bill, and his administration is supporting higher taxes on tobacco. A number of Clinton's top appointments have been known antismoking people.

But Mickey Kantor, the United States trade representative, comes from a law firm deeply involved in tobacco lobbying. Ron Brown, secretary of commerce, likewise is a partner in a law firm that represents tobacco companies. In the past, the offices of these two men have colluded in aggressively promoting American tobacco abroad, and they will need to be carefully watched.

❖   ❖

"Tobacco exports should be expanded aggressively, because Americans are smoking less."

—*DAN QUAYLE, speaking to a group of North Carolina Republicans, 1992*

Dr. William Cahan practiced for fifty years at New York City's famous cancer hospital, Memorial Sloan-Kettering, where he referred to his operating room as "Marlboro Country." His autobiography, *No Stranger to Tears* (1992), is a warmhearted record of his devotion to his work, his family, and his vast number of friends. His ire is reserved entirely for the tobacco industry, which provided him with so many of his patients.

Cahan ceaselessly lectures cabdrivers and friends about smoking ("We're invited to the best houses—once," claims his wife, Grace Mirabella), and speaks out often and publicly in support of antismoking bills. A close friend of many artists, he has had the opportunity to implore scores of famous smokers to quit. His book contains eyewitness accounts of the pitiful ends of many of these same people, such as Leonard Bernstein, Alan Jay Lerner, Babe Ruth, Aline Saarinen, Thomas Schippers, Yul Brynner, and Hubert Humphrey. Over and over Cahan heard, "Why in hell didn't I listen to you."

❖ ❖

"I am haunted not only by the tobacco dead I see but by the lungless, voiceless, bladderless, gulletless, tongueless patients and those close to them who must also suffer."
—WILLIAM G. CAHAN, M.D., **No Stranger to Tears**, *1992*

Joe Milhollin smoked for fifty years and quit only because

his wife wanted to quit. "I took her to shrinks, hypnotists, groups, and the Seventh-Day Adventist program, but she never could quit. I would quit every time myself to help her out, but she'd start up again so I'd smoke too. Finally I said 'The next time I'm quitting for good no matter what you do.' "

Mrs. Milhollin died in 1984 of lung cancer. "She went from flitting around like a bird to just dragging. The doctor would drain her lungs but finally he said, 'Joe, take her home or take her to a convalescent home. She's going to die.' She wanted us to go back to Virginia and see the grandson once more, but she went downhill too fast. She died on our anniversary."

Joe started having breathing trouble a couple of years ago. His doctor first thought it was emphysema, but it turned out to be asbestosis. Joe had joined the Merchant Marine in World War II and remained in through the Vietnam War. Merchant ships were full of asbestos then, and many mariners have come down with asbestosis—nearly all smokers. With medication, Joe's doing well now. It's a lucky thing he's stopped smoking. His girlfriend of the past six years ("the sweetest woman in the world") doesn't like smoking one bit.

❖ ❖

MEDICAL FACT: Cigarette smoking interferes with the lungs' ability to clear asbestos fibers. A synergistic effect on DNA of smoking and asbestos may also contribute to the high asbestosis rate among smokers.

A group of Scandinavian doctors undertook a study of wound healing in smokers and nonsmokers, studying 120 women who had gone under the knife for laparotomy sterilization. The method of suturing was the same for all of them. The doctors compared the width, length, color, and general appearance of the scars. The average-size scar in the smokers was 7.4 millimeters in length; for nonsmokers, it was only 2.7 millimeters. The scars of smokers were more likely to be light in color. The doctors' conclusion was that overall, smokers had significantly worse cosmetic results than nonsmokers.

❖   ❖

"If someone needs a skin flap [a piece of nearby skin redirected over a damaged spot] because of the removal of a skin cancer, and the person smokes, I tell them they can just about forget it. There's not much hope it will take. Skin grafts are also problematical in smokers."

—Dr. Nancy Todes-Taylor, *dermatologist*

Some smokers out there think that they are exempt from the

ultimate horrors brought on by smoking because they don't inhale. They are quite mistaken.

Wherever smoke touches, there's trouble brewing. Noninhalers are at high risk for lip, mouth, tongue, and larynx cancer. Their risks for heart disease and lung cancer are also increased. After all, they're still breathing, and the air that they're breathing is full of smoke. So noninhalers are heavy passive smokers; what's more, a certain amount of the smoke in the mouth leaks down the windpipe even if it isn't sucked down.

It's a puzzle to inhalers why anyone would bother to smoke without inhaling. Mary Pana bothered for forty-nine years and says, "I was a compulsive smoker." She thinks her withdrawal may have been easier than that of an inhaler, but it was by no means easy. And 14 years after quitting, she produced a tumor in her lung—fortunately a tiny one that succumbed to radiation.

❖   ❖

THE ODDS: In one large epidemiological study, male smokers who did not inhale had eight times the lung cancer rate of nonsmokers (versus seventeen times for deep inhalers).

DAY 192 A person who has been diagnosed with lung cancer sometimes feels that it no longer matters whether or not she quits smoking. It does. In the first place, people who continue smoking have five times as many recurrences as those who quit.

Secondarily, those who quit feel a whole lot better. A Lung Cancer Study Group, sponsored by the National Cancer Institute, questioned a number of lung cancer patients who had stopped smoking as to the benefits. They were overwhelmingly enthusiastic. They noted that they breathed more easily, coughed less, and produced less sputum. They felt cleaner and enjoyed food more. They slept better and felt more rested when they awoke.

The psychological benefits were even more gratifying. They felt they looked better, were more in control of their lives, and were proud to have had the will to break the habit.

People who continue smoking after developing lung cancer invite further debilitation. Smoking obstructs the airways and decreases breathing ability. Smokers get more respiratory tract infections and are at higher risk for heart disease and pneumonia.

Nutrition is also extremely important in lung cancer patients, and it is often threatened by nausea and vomiting. While many quitters consider an improved appetite a regrettable side effect, to the cancer patient it can be a critical bonus.

❖ ❖

"Habitual use of tobacco is also wrong because it expends uselessly . . . that which ought to be appropriated to a more valuable purpose."

—JONATHAN A. ALLEN, M.D., 1835

Pipe and cigar smokers have been shown to have life expectancies nearly the same as nonsmokers. Consequently, many cigarette smokers—mostly males—have switched to pipes or cigars. But these gentlemen have not held up so well. It seems that the cigarette smoker turned pipe or cigar smoker is a horse of a different color from the pure pipe or cigar smoker. The ex-cigarette smoker inhales, whatever he's smoking.

A British study of 8,000 men found that among pipe and cigar smokers, those who had never smoked cigarettes had heart attacks at the same rate as nonsmokers. But the ex-cigarette smokers had as many heart attacks as current cigarette smokers. Apparently they might just as well have gone on smoking cigarettes. All cigar and pipe smokers face as well high risks of mouth and throat cancer (an odds ratio of 16.7 times for men who smoke 40-plus cigars and 3.1 times for 40-plus pipefuls of tobacco).

Smokeless tobacco is another bad alternative to cigarettes. Users of snuff and chewing tobacco often have consistently higher levels of nicotine in the bloodstream than cigarette smokers—along with the attendant heart problems.

❖   ❖

"This masculine sucking is beyond understanding for to suck is childish and dribbling is peculiar to children. Waster of time, does this thing nourish you?"
—RICHARD ROWLANDS, 1619

| D A Y   1 9 4 | That a smoker's lung power will decrease due to smoking is |

pretty much guaranteed. Everybody's lung power decreases after 25 or 30 years of age, but the smoker's goes down much faster. Those smokers who doubt this decline should have themselves tested on a spirometer, a simple device which measures how much you exhale. The amount of air expelled is called the FEV_1 (one second forced expiratory volume).

A study of 792 employed men found that the average rate of decline of FEV_1 for never-smokers was 36 mL per year. Those who smoked less than four cigarettes a day averaged a loss of 44 mL per year. At 5 to 15 cigarettes a day, the loss was 46 mL a year. Those who smoked more than 15 cigarettes a day lost 54 mL per year.

Most ex-smokers end up with a rate of decline fairly close to that of never-smokers. However, their overall rate never gets back to what it could have been, unless they smoked for very short periods of time. This is an important reason for young people to quit now rather than later.

THE BRIGHTER SIDE: Although certain kinds of lung damage can never be repaired, ex-smokers improve so much in the cardiovascular department that some of them go on to run marathons.

The 1971 ban on radio and TV advertising of cigarettes

was a bonanza for magazines. By 1983, their revenues from tobacco ads were 727 percent higher (adjusted for inflation) than they had been in 1969.

Meanwhile, what had happened to the public's right to know? Suddenly, magazines found news about smoking and health a lot less interesting than it had been pre-1971. In magazines that carried cigarette advertising, coverage of smoking and health fell 65 percent. Even the lofty *New York Times* ran 21 percent fewer articles on smoking when the revenues went up.

On the other hand, the *Christian Science Monitor*, which does not take cigarette ads, continued its reportage on smoking nearly as before. And the *Reader's Digest*, which has long eschewed tobacco ads, found something worth saying about smoking in 34 percent of its health articles over a 26-year period.

Redbook Magazine, heavily reliant on tobacco ads, between 1970 and 1981 produced zero articles on smoking and health. *Cosmopolitan* ran one article on smoking between 1981 and 1986—reporting that heavy smokers ran a lower risk of endometrial cancer!

It's not that there wasn't any news. On every health front—cancer, pregnancy, addictiveness, heart disease—evidence against smoking was piling up. The smoker can be excused if he missed a lot of it. He wasn't told.

❖   ❖

TOBACCO POWER: *Ms. Magazine, a self-proclaimed leader on women's health, from 1972 to 1985 ran 583 pages of cigarette ads and zero articles on smoking. To its credit, Ms. no longer takes advertising of any kind.*

| D A Y   1 9 6 | Athletics have always been im-
portant to Ben Wootten, a fi-
nancial advisor. In college he skied and played soccer, and
felt only slightly the worse for his pack-and-a-half-a-day smoking
habit. But a few years later, bouts of bronchitis persuaded him
to switch to a pipe—which he admits to having smoked twelve
hours a day.

In 1977 he gave up his pipe. He was rewarded with unexpected benefits. "It's been a lot easier to stay in shape over the
past fifteen years," he says. "I can take a week away from
workouts, and it's much less painful to get back in again.

"I remember running for the first time here [in Maine] in the
spring after quitting, and noticing that I could smell the apple
blossoms. It made me feel as if I were 15 again, which was
the last time I could smell them, before I started smoking. I realized then that I'd been missing a whole sequence of smells
through the seasons, from the apple blossoms to the lilacs and
so on. The damp smell on the second green of the golf course
took me back to age 15, too.

"I can't say I miss my pipe. Right now, it would char my
mouth. To enjoy it, I'd have to build up calluses on my tongue
and palate again. My mouth is now back in some reasonable
pre-cancerous condition."

❖ ❖

*THE ODDS: A pipe smoker has 3.6 times the chance of getting
cancer of the esophagus as nonsmokers. He also has a much
higher risk for oral cancers than cigarette smokers.*

Cigarette smoking has a sinister effect on pregnancy. Because nicotine rapidly circulates to all parts of the body, a fetus can be exposed to substantial nicotine levels, producing a higher rate of miscarriage, lower average birthweight, and various birth-related problems. Prenatal nicotine exposure also corresponds with increased tremors in newborns, more muscular tension, and more nervous system excitation.

A study by the National Institute for Drug Abuse found that at one year of age, nicotine babies had lower developmental scores and poorer auditory responses than nonsmoking babies. Two-year-olds had cognitive deficiencies—but whether because of their prenatal or their postnatal environments has not been positively determined.

❖ ❖

"It is possible that the fetus may also become physically dependent on nicotine and that prenatal nicotine exposure may be a risk factor for later development of tobacco and other psychoactive substance dependency, but no studies on these effects have been reported."

—NATIONAL INSTITUTE ON DRUG ABUSE,
The Third Trienniel Report to Congress, *1991*

We've noted before that people who cut down on the number or kind of cigarettes they smoke rarely do themselves much good. What is amazing is how effectively they can compensate by smoking more furiously.

In one group studied, smokers on reduced cigarette rations managed to take in three times as many toxins as they were supposed to from each remaining cigarette. For instance, a smoker who went from 37 cigarettes a day to five a day decreased his intake of carbon monoxide by only 50 percent.

Likewise, smokers who switch to lower nicotine brands can smoke harder and do themselves as much damage as they did before. In fact, "light" smokers of "light" cigarettes can actually be quite heavy smokers.

❖   ❖

"I smoked very little. But one day my plane arrived late in the Atlanta airport and I had to run like crazy to make my connection. I got a sharp pain in my chest that lasted for three days, and I knew it was from smoking. So I quit. What surprised me was how glad my son was about my quitting. So I thought, 'Well, my not smoking makes him happier than smoking ever made me, so I won't go back to it.' And I didn't."

—*SANDY B., ex-smoker*

Pancreatic cancer has arrived
on the list of smoking-related

cancers. Major epidemiological studies, adjusted for other factors, show smokers with two to three times the chance of dying of this cancer. (Meat eating and alcohol drinking are also risks for pancreatic cancer.) The rate of pancreatic cancer has been fast rising and is today one of the top five causes of cancer death.

In autopsies, the pancreatic duct cells of smokers show atypical changes in their nuclei. Either bile or blood could have delivered the tobacco carcinogens.

In pancreatic cancer, symptoms arrive late, and fewer than 2 percent of the sufferers last five years. Former smokers have lower rates than active smokers—a clue that the association between smoking and pancreatic cancer is not coincidental—and their risks fall to normal within ten to fifteen years.

❖   ❖

"It is just such an outrageous infuriating idea that people smoke cigarettes that it's hard to talk about in rational terms. Everyone has the right to do what they want to their own body, but what I see is all the families who suffer as they watch their loved ones die and are left alone. I can't imagine anything more selfish than smoking cigarettes."
—DR. STEVEN A. ROSENBERG,
Chief of Surgery, National Cancer Institute

| D A Y   2 0 0 | Carol Sergio Coy was a strikingly beautiful woman who

had her first baby when she was forty years old. Shortly after the birth, she was stricken with terrible pains. That's when she discovered that she had lung cancer. A lung was immediately removed. She died two and a half years later, on October 4, 1991.

Carol was a nonsmoker. Why lung cancer? The answer is that she had been a flight attendant for American Airlines for twenty years. Airplanes are terrible traps for smoke, and the ban on smoking on domestic flights came too late for Carol and many other victims on airline crews.

Smoking continues on American Airlines on flights to Hawaii and Mexico and on other airlines on overseas flights. Ninety-three percent of flight attendants report adverse effects from smoke. As this book goes to press, Americans for Nonsmokers' Rights and other groups are campaigning for smoke-free international flights.

❖ ❖

"Carol died just five years from the day we met and four years after we married. She lived as long as she did because of a tremendous will, and despite the suffering, they were wonderful years. Now my son and I have lost her because of a situation that should never have been allowed to exist— smoking on airplanes."

—MIKE COY, 1992

It is said that many months after
withdrawal crack addicts will

suddenly revert to what seems like early-stage craving. And so
it is with cigarette addicts. Even years after quitting, the impulse
to smoke can come crashing to the fore, and it will seem that
nothing matters more than a cigarette.

Part of this is because the modern cigarette is such a successful product. With a pipe you have to cram the tobacco in,
get the thing going, puff for a while, and wait for the cheeks
to absorb the nicotine. Not so with the cigarette. Light it up
and bang! The tobacco is in your lungs, which, having a surface area about the size of a tennis court, absorb smoke mar-
velously. And on to the brain! For a few seconds your troubles
seem over, until you realize that you're holding one of the horrible things again, it's making you feel sick, and all your worst
fears about your own character are confirmed. Don't do it. If
you were sorry once that you smoked, you'll be a lot sorrier
now.

❖   ❖

*"I have never smoked in my life and look forward to a time
when the world will look back in amazement and disgust
to a practice so unnatural and offensive."*
—GEORGE BERNARD SHAW, 1946

Cancer of the larynx is another of the unpleasant fates lying in wait for smokers. It's a disease that nonsmokers don't have to worry about. But in smokers, cells with atypical nuclei begin to grow in the larynx, then become a localized cancer, and then an invasive one. Laryngeal cancer is nasty. Many people die from it, and many more lose their vocal cords.

It takes three to four years for the risk from laryngeal cancer to go down after quitting, and ten years to approach the risk of the never-smoker. Younger and younger people are succumbing to laryngeal cancer; it is not unusual for people in their forties to be stricken.

Hoarseness is an early symptom; anyone hoarser than usual for two weeks should see a doctor. This is just as true for people (like yourself) who have quit smoking. With early treatment, not only can your life be saved, but you can keep your vocal cords as well.

❖   ❖

FACT: *Only 30 percent of heavy smokers have normal cells lining their vocal cords.*

Stress is a prime reason that smokers give for smoking.

When pipes were the usual way to smoke, smoking was a leisure-time activity. In fast-paced modern life, smoking goes along with all the high-pressure moments. Cigarettes, as the handiest and most efficient delivery system for the drug, suit the busy person's schedule well.

It is likely that one of the reasons that smoking is now becoming largely a blue-collar activity is that the unprofessional life is so stressful. Doctors and lawyers endure high stress, but they have choices in their lives and enough money to pay the mortgage. The life of someone short of rent money, without medical insurance, and marginally employed is even more stressful.

The sad thing is that smoking doesn't relieve stress. It only makes people stop thinking about it for a few minutes. Then the stress wells up again, just as big as before. What relieves stress are all the things you do when you're not smoking, which are just the things that smokers are less likely to get around to doing.

❖ ❖

"[Tobacco] renders a man oblivious for the moment to fatigue, business cares, domestic and social felicities, and other causes of psychic distress, but nobody has even suggested that tobacco cures any of these ills."

—JOHN HARVEY KELLOGG, M.D., Tobaccoism, 1929

A typical cigarette fire starts in a mattress. A spark falls. Or the smoker goes to sleep, cigarette in hand. The fire quietly smolders, almost unnoticeably, for hours. There is little sign of the catastrophe mounting within the mattress until it bursts into giant flames.

When firefighters find smoldering mattresses, they rip them apart. Civilians, unfortunately, often think they've extinguished a fire when it's still burning where the eye can't see.

New codes have required that mattresses and upholstered furniture be manufactured out of fire-retardant material, but such material can only discourage fires, not prevent them altogether. What's more, the smokers' clothes and bedding are apt to burn easily. And many people are still sleeping on the old flammable mattresses. It's a death any ex-smoker can be glad to have avoided.

❖ ❖

TOBACCO POWER: *Furniture made of regulation polyurethane materials, resistant to catching fire from smoldering cigarettes, burns faster and hotter when set on fire by an open flame. The fumes from these "plastic" fires are also much more toxic than normal fumes. It's only because of cigarettes that furniture must be made with these problematical coverings. It would be far more logical to require that cigarettes be self-extinguishing than that the couches be smolder-resistant, but the tobacco industry regulates the regulators.*

Amidst all the statistics of death and mayhem wrought by ciga-

rettes, we all can point to examples of survivors. There's Uncle Hank, age 88, who smoked since he was 14, hale and hearty still. Well, maybe he's no mountain goat, but what do you expect at 88? And Grandma—the photographer at the nursing home made her put her cigarette down when he took her picture on her hundredth birthday.

You may have to look a little harder to find an old smoker in good spirits. A lifetime of inhaling a depressant is likely to drag down even upbeat personalities. Even so, there are a couple of cheerful old smokers around.

But imagine the disappointment when a smoker discovers that he wasn't fated to be in this tiny circle of happy old smokers. It can happen at the worst moment. You've just found the love of your life . . . retired and started doing what you've always wanted to—sold your first book to a publisher—when boom: "I'm afraid it's inoperable," says the doctor.

"It is of no consequence that there are honest men who use tobacco steadily and still live a long life and keep their mental alertness. My answer is, as one swallow does not make a spring, so one or two exceptions do not refute the everyday experience of men."
—JACOB JOSEPH JOEPSER, Guide to Longer Life, *1680*

There are some who think that there's an element of fanaticism in some of the newfound loathing of tobacco. But those who seem fanatic now would merely have been normal in the Victorian era.

Captain Crawley, a penniless character in Thackeray's *Vanity Fair* (1848), hopes to better himself through acquaintance with his rich great-aunt. A visit to her case goes nicely, until he is brought down by his aunt's loathing of tobacco.

"Nobody could smell the tobacco, he thought, if he cunningly opened the window and kept his head and pipe in the fresh air." This he did, but he had forgotten that his door was open all the time "so that the breeze blew the clouds of tobacco downstairs and arrived with quite undiminished fragrance to Miss Crawley and Miss Briggs."

That pipe of tobacco finished the business. A note arrived the next morning: " 'Dear Sir, Miss Crawley has passed an exceedingly disturbed night, owing to the shocking manner in which the house has been polluted by tobacco; Miss Crawley begs me to say that she regrets that she is too unwell to see you before you go.' And herewith honest James's career as a candidate for his aunt's favor ended."

❖ ❖

An Early Grave: King George VI, the father of the present queen of England, died of lung cancer in 1952 at the age of 57. He himself blamed his smoking for his disease, showing an intuition many doctors lacked at the time.

The tobacco industry regularly
denies that it markets to chil-

dren. Just what, then, is the point of the Joe Camel advertising?
Old Joe the Camel is a popular character with kids. One study
found that 91 percent of six-year-olds knew that Old Joe went
with cigarettes, and even 30 percent of the three-year-olds
questioned recognized Old Joe.

Market researchers generally believe that brand awareness
created in childhood creates preferences for adulthood. Cigarette makers do not even have to wait for adulthood as a large
proportion of smokers pick up their first cigarette before age
14. A few short years ago, this cigarette was hardly ever a
Camel. Practically the only people who smoked Camels were
old people. Three years after the Old Joe campaign began,
Camels became the choice of 32.8 percent of under-18s who
smoke—a market share of $476 million per year.

Was this unintentional? Did RJR Nabisco (the makers of
Camel cigarettes) really think that Old Joe would go over with
adults and be ignored by children? If so, why were the themes
of Old Joe ("a smooth character") exploitive of the peer insecu-
rity that so many children feel between ages 12 and 16?

❖   ❖

*"Where I worked we were trying very hard to influence
kids who were 14 to start to smoke."*
                              —*Anonymous advertising consultant,*
                              quoted in The Journal of the American
                              Medical Association, *1991*

| D A Y   2 0 8 | Colon cancer is not usually blamed on smoking, but there

is evidence of a correlation. For a study of colon polyps, 549 white men, all of whom were pattern makers, underwent sigmoidoscopies. One or more colon polyps were detected in 76 of the men.

Of those who had never smoked, 9 percent had colon polyps. Of ex-smokers, 12 percent had polyps. Among current smokers, 21 percent had colon polyps. The rates increased with the number of cigarettes smoked per day and the number of pack years in the individual smoking history; this was true even for the ex-smokers.

The findings are significant because colon polyps are a precursor of colon cancer. Colon cancer can be very unpleasant. It's best avoided.

FACT: *Of the 4,000 compounds found in cigarettes, some are so toxic—such as tobacco-specific nitrosamines, benzoapyrene, and formaldehyde—that sale in other forms is either prohibited or regulated.*

A 1981 study compared a group of women who had

spontaneous abortions to a group who carried their pregnancies to 28 weeks or more. (From the spontaneous abortion group, the study excluded fetuses that showed evidence of chromosomal abnormalities.) The odds for a spontaneous abortion increased 46 percent for the first ten cigarettes smoked per day; they went up 61 percent for the first twenty cigarettes smoked.

Another threat to pregnancy, placenta previa, is twice as common in smokers. Placenta previa is a condition in which a serious hemorrhage occurs late in pregnancy due to a placenta that is too low in the uterus. The latest study found that the length of the smoking history was not important; the risk pertained only to women who smoked during the pregnancy itself.

❖   ❖

A Smoker's Life: One-third of the children in families with incomes over $40,000 are exposed to cigarette smoke as opposed to two-thirds of the children in families with incomes under $10,000.

| D A Y   2 1 0 | Larry Schwartz is on the patch now. Twenty years ago he quit smoking and stayed quit for three years, during which he taught for Smokenders. Three months after he stopped teaching, he started smoking again.

Why? "I was away for a weekend, working, and there wasn't much to do. There was a pack of cigarettes sitting in front of me, and I was bored so I had one. The trap is that the first cigarette does nothing so you think you're okay. And you have a second and a third, and in two weeks you're smoking just as you always did."

The patch is wonderful, says Larry. "It takes the strong edge off the desire and separates the mental out from the physical. I go to a group too that will keep on meeting for a year. Which is important because the first month after stopping is not as hard as the third month or the seventh month."

❖ ❖

THE BRIGHT SIDE: *In the United States, half the people who have ever smoked have quit.*

B. F. Skinner, the famous behavioral psychologist, re-

mained productive until his death at age 86. When he was
78, he wrote a book called *Enjoy Old Age*, based on his own
experience in what he called "the country of old age."

He suggested that we'd all enjoy our lives more in the country of old age if we prepared ourselves before we went. Unfortunately, he said, this country is one people seldom want to
know about. It looks too much like a dreary wasteland, and no
one wants to think about being old. So old age often comes
as an unpleasant surprise. One way of planning for old age is
to quit smoking.

❖   ❖

*"Young people themselves often make the prospect more dismal
by viewing old age as the time when they will pay the debts
they have incurred while young. They go on smoking
cigarettes and defer the lung cancer to a never-never
land of the future. They convert old age into a kind of dumping
ground for hazardous waste. . . . Old age is not all that bad,
and planning can make it better."*

—B. F. SKINNER AND M. E. VAUGHAN,
Enjoy Old Age, 1983

| D A Y 2 1 2 | Smokers are more likely than nonsmokers to have ectopic

(tubal) pregnancies. In a Washington state study, smoking under ten cigarettes a day increased a woman's chance of ectopic pregnancy to 1.4 that of a nonsmoker; women who smoked a pack and a half a day had five times the risk. For former smokers who had quit within the last eight years, the risk was 1.6; over time the rate of former smokers dropped to that of never-smokers.

❖   ❖

"Of all the plants that Tellus bosom yields
In Groves, Glades, Gardens, Marshes, Mountains, Fields,
None so pernicious to Man's life is known,
As is Tobacco, saving hemp alone.
Betwixt which two there seem great sympathy,
To ruin poor Adam's progeny."
                              —JOSHUAH SYLVESTER, **Tobacco Battered**, 1616

Nicotine, when distilled, is a powerful poison. The diarist

Samuel Pepys reported in 1665 that he had witnessed an experiment in which a drop of oil of nicotine killed a cat. Regrettably, the experiment has been repeated many times since.

In 1899, the English medical magazine *Lancet* raised the subject of whether all tobacco shouldn't be sold as poison. A certain pesticide marketed at the time was made up of 37 percent nicotine, 44 percent camphor, and 15 percent alcohol; nicotine was the deadly ingredient. The poor man who manufactured it—having had too close a brush with his own product—had become paralyzed.

The only reason smokers live as long as they do is that the amount of nicotine in a single cigarette is very small, and smokers build tolerance to it. Nonetheless, these small doses of poison are circulating to every cell of the body, along with the many other deadly chemicals in tobacco. The damage is cumulative.

❖ ❖

FACT: The urine of cigarette smokers exhibits at least twice the mutagenic activity as nonsmokers' urine.

"My parents both smoked Chesterfields, and I still remember the radio ad for them," says Mark Dowie. "First there'd be the sound of someone coughing, and then a voice would break in and say that here was a person who needed to switch to Chesterfields. My parents seemed paragons of health to me so I started with Chesterfields."

Dowie started young (age eight) but never became a big smoker. "My coaches in high school all said, 'You want to play, you don't smoke.' But nobody ever said anything about cancer. Then in college I didn't smoke during the lacrosse season. After college, five a day were still usually enough for me unless I went to a party, when I would smoke half a pack and wake up the next day with a sickly hangover. Since I quit, I don't get that kind of hangover anymore, unless I'm around people who are smoking a lot.

"Then the whole health thing hit. My father quit smoking, and I thought, well, if he could, I could. Little as I smoked, it wasn't easy. I did it by putting off the time I started to an hour later each day. Then I got a bad cold and never smoked again. My wind noticeably improved afterwards, and I started running ten-kilometer races in respectable time.

"My mother smoked until she got lung cancer and had a lung removed. She died in 1987. It was very sad; she should have lived much longer."

❖ ❖

An Ally: Vice President Al Gore's family gave up growing tobacco when Gore's sister died of lung cancer.

The cilia, the little hairlike for-

mations that clean the airways,
are embedded in mucus. One group of medical researchers actually went so far as to compare the mucus in the windpipes of smokers and nonsmokers.

The mucus samples were collected during bronchoscopies. The samples from the smokers proved to be less elastic than those from nonsmokers, and thus less easily clearable. The degree of resistance to coughing increased with greater tobacco consumption, and the most difficult to clear was mucus from people with cancer.

The researchers felt that their findings jibed with the hypothesis that people who can't clear their mucus are more apt to get lung cancer. Quitting smoking improves the state of the mucus, although not quickly.

❖ ❖

"The doctors tell me that I have maybe five or six weeks to go because I have lung cancer caused by smoking.

"You face more danger with the twenty cigarettes that are in your pocket than any six bullets in somebody's gun. Cigarettes are a time bomb that you plant in your own life that explode 20 or 30 years later. . . . The danger that threatened my life as a policeman was sitting in that radio car and lighting up that cigarette. I am 47 years old, and I'll never see 48."

—KEN McFEELY, *New York City policeman,
in radio spot made by Tony Schwartz, 1987*

| D A Y   2 1 6 | "Not a large number of people ultimately survive any of the smoking-related cancers," says Dr. Bruce Trock, cancer epidemiologist. "Most aerodigestive tract cancers—such as lung, esophagus, and oral cancers—are fatal unless diagnosed at an early stage, and early diagnosis is unlikely for lung and esophagus cancers.

"For many of the head and neck cancers the treatment can be devastating, with severe effects on appearance and an impact on tasting, eating, and smelling. Often by the time the cancer is noticeable you already have microscopic spread of tumor cells beyond the original area, which makes the chance of curing the tumor decrease drastically. Some people end up getting multiple primary tumors. After all, you're bathing the mouth, throat, and lungs in smoke containing more than forty carcinogens.

"A lot of the oral cancers do give early warning signs. If they're detected in time the surgery can be relatively minor, but smokers are often not very health-conscious and will ignore early symptoms. Anything other than a small oral tumor can require very major surgery, including removal of portions of the tongue or the jaw or other very disfiguring operations. I think if more smokers saw pictures of people who had had head and neck surgery, it would dissuade them from smoking."

❖   ❖

WORD TO THE WISE: A good dentist looks hard for mouth cancers and is your best resource for detecting them at a curable stage. Have regular checkups, because as a recent ex-smoker you are still at risk.

You may occasionally think to yourself that a cigarette would

DAY 217

be nice. This is the kind of thought that you didn't get to indulge in when you smoked—smokers don't choose to smoke; they *must* smoke. At their elbows, every waking moment, is the Addiction, reminding them 10 or 20 or 30 or 40 or more times a day that it's time for a cigarette. If put off, the buzz of the Addiction gets louder and louder, until the poor smoker can hardly think of anything other than the next cigarette.

So be grateful. You are now in a position to think rationally about how it would not be nice to have the Addiction move back in, stuck to you like a Siamese twin. This is what is meant by freedom from cigarettes. Your timetable is your own.

❖   ❖

"One of the reasons I'm really glad that I've stopped smoking is that stopping was a big thing on the list of things that I knew I had to do in my life. Now I've gotten to cross it off my list."

—SUZANNE MANTELL, *ex-smoker*

| D A Y   2 1 8 | Smokers tend to feel that smoking helps them concentrate,

and there's a modicum of evidence showing that it does. It's not much good for the big, important things—no showing of better books written by smokers—but it does apparently aid and abet when there's some really boring work to do. When stuck doing something repetitive, smokers (in some tests) don't get as maddened by the task as nonsmokers and don't become distracted as easily.

But is this so wonderful? Not only is the smoker shirking his human responsibility to be infuriated by inhuman work, he is plodding through life ignoring to some degree what's around him. In the abstract, we admire people who aren't distracted, but are they really the people we would like to see Rome with?

Just possibly, the smoker's tolerance of boredom is making him just a bit boring himself. By concentrating on smoking, smokers miss a lot of the action in life, and smoking promotes procrastination as well. You become more interesting when you don't smoke.

❖   ❖

FORGOTTEN BUT NOT GONE: People entering a smokers' room long after the smokers have left it will still be exposed to the harmful particles and gases found in tobacco smoke.

Young children whose parents smoke have more middle ear

infections than children whose homes are smoke free. A 1992 study followed 132 preschoolers at a day-care center at the University of North Carolina. The results corroborated previous studies.

Smoke exposure in the children was established by measuring cotinine levels in the blood. Cotinine is a reliable marker for nicotine and produces a much more accurate record of smoking than interviews do. The 87 children with high cotinine levels developed 38 percent more middle ear infections during their first three years than the other 45 children.

Furthermore, infections lasted an average of 28 days for the kids with smoke in the house, and only 19 days for the others. "Children exposed to tobacco smoke had a harder time breaking loose from the infection cycle," said researcher Nancy Haley. It is notable that these particular children spent their days in a smokefree place; problems are doubtless worse for children spending days and nights in smoke-filled homes.

❖   ❖

A SMOKER'S LIFE: Smokers have more hearing loss than nonsmokers, according to a recent Egyptian study. The ears are vulnerable to smoke damage through the eustachian tube, by which they're connected to the throat. Those people allergic to tobacco smoke fare the worst, as smoke can cause eustachian tube blockages and sinus trouble. But even in nonallergic people, smoke can damage the delicate structures of the inner ear.

| D A Y   2 2 0 | Cigarettes have a lot in them besides the "selected fine to-
baccos" listed on the package. Every brand has added
texturizers, flavorants, and preservatives. As a number of these
are carcinogenic, smokers might wish to shop around when
they pick a brand. They can't. But the ingredients are secret:
American manufacturers are only required to hand over a
vague list of their secret ingredients to the Office of Smoking
and Health, and the list may not be released publicly. Senator
Edward Kennedy has characterized the information in it as "effectively useless."

Canadian companies are far more regulated, and since
1989 cigarette manufacturers have to submit recipes for each
brand to government health officials. This was asking too much
of R.J. Reynolds and Philip Morris, which took their cigarettes
off the Canadian market when the law passed. (R.J. Reynolds
eventually made a comeback with a cigarette reformulated for
Canadians.)

The Canadian lists reveal that you may find shellac, ace-
tone, turpentine, acetaldehyde, glyoxal, and methylsalicylate
added to your cigarettes. None of these are savory, and there
are a great many others, such as caramel, which are benign
until burned, whereupon they become carcinogenic. We are
unlikely to ever know what is found in American cigarettes.
Keeping its ingredients secret is one of the tobacco industry's
many special privileges.

❖   ❖

*"The question that I think I would ask if I were an American
is, what is it that American tobacco companies don't want
the Canadian government to know about American
cigarettes, to the point where they're willing to stop
shipping their product to Canada altogether?"*

—NEIL COLLISHAW, The Nation, *December 23, 1991*

A bookie might not look at Patricia Arnold as a top con-

tender to never smoke again because 1) she smoked over a pack a day and 2) she really loved smoking. But in fact she's a great bet. What she's got is determination. Nine months ago, on January 1, 1993, she put smoking behind her and made up her mind that it was for good. Six months of planning preceded the event.

"Everything to do with smoking is pleasurable, which makes it difficult to quit," says Arnold, a medical administrator. "You just have to get by that. There are a lot of compensations. My time is my own again, and I like that. I don't have to keep stopping to smoke. I don't have to worry about having my cigarettes around. And anyone has to be glad not to be living with the smell.

"I miss smoking. I don't know if I'll ever be over that. But I'll never smoke again. That I know. I found out the last time I quit that I can't smoke just one. I come from a family of six children, and we all smoked, and I was the last to quit. My husband quit six weeks ago, though I told him, 'Don't do it for me.' You have to quit for yourself. I just hope my daughter never starts. Maybe she won't because she's seen what I've gone through in quitting."

❖ ❖

Sad Fact: Half of all smoking deaths strike people in middle age; these middle-aged victims on average lose twenty-three years of life.

Dr. Henry Gibbons won a prize in 1868 for writing *Tobacco and Its Effects*, a pamphlet that covers a good part of the ground that the American Cancer Society smoking pamphlets cover now—and in more elegant language. Dr. Gibbons knew about the fatty heart, angina pectoris, the devitalized blood to the brain, and the loss of virility. He missed lung cancer, the fetal nicotine syndrome, and wrinkles, but in his day women didn't smoke and the cigarette epidemic (which brought so much lung cancer) hadn't yet arrived.

Dr. Gibbons is particularly good on the subtleties of addiction: "That [tobacco] brings relief and comfort to those who have trained themselves to depend on it for relief and comfort is measurably true. But the suffering it relieves is the suffering it has created. It is a blessing only where it has first become a curse. Persons who avoid the habit never suffer the want.

"When a lamp is exhausted we supply it with oil. Without oil a temporary flame may be produced by raising the wick; but the wick itself is consumed. So with the lamp of life, when instead of food we resort to stimulants. There is always a penalty lying in wait."

❖ ❖

"Tobacco is conducive to indolence, both physical and moral."
—DR. HENRY GIBBONS, **Tobacco and Its Effects**, *1868*

Drug addiction is a big field of

study, and nicotine addicts fit
the model. 1) There's a reproducible withdrawal syndrome;
and 2) to prevent relapse, the behavior must be treated. As
with morphine addicts, the majority of smokers go back to
smoking within a few months after withdrawal.

One Abraham Winkler observed in 1948 that ex-addicts,
even when physiological withdrawal was long past, still reported withdrawal symptoms (such as craving) in the face of
certain stimuli. As does the ex-smoker. Just as Pavlov's dogs sal-
ivated on hearing a bell, the ex-smoker longs for cigarettes
when various metaphoric bells ring.

Behavioral change consists of substituting something else for
lighting up when the bell rings. You've already been doing this,
or you wouldn't have made it to Day 223. And if you still have
bad moments, try to figure out what bell is ringing and how to
answer without smoking. The whole trick of remaining a nonsmoker lies in coping with these bells.

❖   ❖

TODAY'S TIP: *A tip from the old-timers in Alcoholics
Anonymous: "HALT! Don't get too Hungry, Angry, Lonely,
or Tired."*

Canada has dealt much more militantly with smoking than the U.S.A.—and with more success. Canadians used to smoke more than Americans but now are down to 1,800 cigarettes per capita; the comparable rate in the U.S.A. is 2,023. Between 1984 and 1991, the Canadian rate of decline was twice that in the U.S.A.

Besides a tax on cigarettes ten times ours, which raises the price to about $6 a pack, all cigarette advertising was banned in Canada in 1989. Garfield Mahood of Canada's Nonsmokers' Rights Association calls this "moving society toward informed consent.

"For informed consent you have to eliminate tobacco disinformation, which is what tobacco advertising is—the implication that you can be healthy and cross-country ski and do aerobics when you're a smoker. Then you have to increase information by bringing in an effective warning system. What is on most cigarette packs in the world is a joke." Coming up in Canada is a big prominent black-and-white box on cigarette packages, complete with a warning that smoking is addictive, and warning inserts inside the package. "This will be a warning system that is intended to warn," says Mahood, "rather than one that is intended to protect the industry from product litigation."

❖   ❖

"No person shall advertise any tobacco product offered for sale in Canada."
—Section 4,
The Tobacco Products Control Act, January 1, 1989

Kate Cloudsparks quit smoking in 1981. She was a hospital

nurse and, odd as it seems, a lot of nurses then still smoked. "We'd spend the night shift drinking coffee and smoking cigarettes," says Kate.

In this milieu, quitting was hard, but there was inspiration as well. "I've never forgotten one of the patients," Kate recounts, "who was in her last two or three days of emphysema. Her lips were blue. She would have us turn off her oxygen so that she could smoke a cigarette. She said there was no use in her quitting at that point. A lot of the staff agreed with her, although there were some who refused to turn off the oxygen."

Besides that sad picture, Kate didn't like her own coughing and smell and shortness of breath. What's more, she was about to go to graduate school, and cigarettes loomed as an unaffordable luxury in her reduced budget. So she quit. "It wasn't quite as bad as I thought it would be. I was ready. Growing up, I'd hated smoking as both my parents were chain-smokers, and I didn't want to go on smoking for the rest of my life."

❖   ❖

"The only thing good about tobacco is that it chases the mosquitoes away, which just goes to show that mosquitoes are smarter than people."

—WILL ROGERS

The decline in smoking in the U.S.A. has sent cigarette companies to the Third World to find new customers. Penetrating the closed markets of these countries is difficult, but the sales potential is enormous.

Where markets are closed, tobacco sales are restricted to a national monopoly or firm. The cigarettes are usually harsh, high-priced, and unadvertised. Typically, many men smoke but at a much lower rate than in the West, and few women or adolescents smoke or could afford to.

China is now the juiciest apple on the tree in the eyes of the tobacco industry. With over a billion people, and the majority nonsmokers, the market appears gravely underexploited. Only 7 percent of the women smoke, and general knowledge of health hazards is scanty. The Beijing government has agreed (under duress) to start importing American cigarettes in 1995, and Marlboro has already succeeded in making its name famous in China.

❖   ❖

"Some monopolies regard their duty as being to do no more than make their tobacco products passively available to smokers who want them; newcomers, domestic or foreign, usually feel need for more dynamic marketing, aided by thrusting advertisements of a kind that may be new to the target market."
—M. F. BARFORD, Tobacco Journal International, 1991

Analyzing someone's saliva is a surefire way of picking out a

smoker. A newly developed sputum cytology test, the Saccommano technique, identifies eight different problem areas in the smoker's sputum—including abnormal cells and chromosomal changes. This test can furthermore identify malignant and precancerous cells, thus serving as an early warning system for people at risk for lung and mouth cancers, which all smokers are.

Men who smoke have up to 18 times the chance of getting cancer of the lip, tongue, palate, gum, or pharynx; pipes, cigars, and smokeless tobacco contribute heavily to the rate. The risk is lower for smokers of filtered cigarettes, and women smokers stand a mere six times the risk of nonsmokers. One might imagine that a mouth cancer could be easily removed, but in fact total recovery is rare. While the number of deaths from oral cancer is not great (6,402 in 1988), they are nearly all unnecessary.

❖   ❖

A SMOKER'S LIFE: Musical comedy's most successful composer, Richard Rodgers (South Pacific, Oklahoma!, The Sound of Music) smoked two and a half packs a day. He developed a cancer that required the combined removal of parts of his jawbone and mouth along with his lymph nodes. This surgery left him disfigured but functional. Some years later, he was stricken with a new primary cancer of the vocal cords. This time, surgery left him voiceless, although he did master the technique of speaking through burps.

`DAY 228` American tobacco companies
have a long row to hoe when
they eye countries with closed markets and low-key sales of cigarettes. Their goal is to eliminate import quotas and to expand
the market through full-throttle advertising and promotion. The government in question usually would prefer to discourage smoking.

Tobacco companies try to warm up their reception by supporting local politicians and charities. But the real pressure
comes from the United States Trade Representative, which can
threaten to impose high tariffs on exports from countries that
"unfairly" restrict import of U.S. cigarettes.

Acting for the tobacco companies, the United States Trade
Representative between 1985 and 1990 threatened Japan,
Taiwan, South Korea, and Thailand with retaliatory tariffs. Japan,
Taiwan, and South Korea capitulated and accepted American
cigarettes, complete with full-blown advertising campaigns. Cigarette consumption immediately increased. Thailand gallantly resisted, with assistance from antismoking organizations
worldwide. American cigarettes are now sold in Thailand, but
companies are not allowed to advertise, promote, or even display their wares. Thus the damage is minimalized.

❖ ❖

*"Japan's friends in Congress will have a better chance to
stem the tide of anti-Japanese trade sentiment if and when
they can cite tangible examples of your doors being
opened to American products. . . . May I suggest a goal
of 20 percent [market for U.S. cigarettes] within the next
18 months?"*

—SENATOR JESSE HELMS OF NORTH CAROLINA TO HIS
EXCELLENCY YASUHIRO NAKASONE,
Prime Minister of Japan, 1986

The last of the recalcitrant smokers lights up a cigarette at

DAY 229

the lunch counter. Five seats down, a chunky lady starts conspicuously waving the smoke away, turns to the smoker, and says, "Pleeease."

The smoker is infuriated. Is one little cigarette going to kill this lady, who should be worrying instead about her own obvious problem of overeating? "The fat lady is smart," says Dr. Stanton Glantz, an authority on passive smoking at the University of California.

"One cigarette puts enough pollution in the air to violate the federal Clean Air Act. Nobody's saying that it's the same thing as putting a gun to your head, but it can hurt you."

❖ ❖

LEGAL DEPARTMENT: *A nonsmoking California waiter received an $85,000 settlement in a workmen's compensation case— enough to pay his medical bills for his heart attack, which he claimed was brought on by working in a smoky restaurant/bar. The waiter, Avtar Uhbi, a vegetarian, had otherwise no risk factors for heart disease. He has since opened his own restaurant, Avtar's in Sausalito, which is smoke free and largely vegetarian.*

If you want to die, and already have high blood pressure and high cholesterol, smoke. You can then enter a category with a coronary death rate ten times above normal. Beta-blockers probably won't work on you.

Many confirmed smokers become scared enough to quit when big trouble is diagnosed. For those with coronary bypasses coming up, it is well worth knocking off cigarettes six months ahead of the operation. One study followed 200 patients through their coronary bypasses, taking detailed respiratory, cardiovascular, and smoking histories. The patients were assessed throughout the postoperative period for complications.

Patients who had quit smoking less than two months before their operations had four times the complications of those who had stopped for more than two months (57 percent versus 14 percent). Those who stopped six months before the operation had complications similar to those who had never smoked (11 percent).

❖ ❖

"The most effective method of smoking cessation is a heart attack. Of those who survive, 50 percent quit smoking over the long term."
—WILLIAM J. MCCARTHY, *UCLA research psychologist*

DJ Mike Fain works in a night-club. "Everyone I know smokes," he says. His circles represent an unfortunate fact about today's smokers—many are young.

DJ Mike, however, used to be a lifeguard and when he was 27, he took up swimming again. "If you want to quit smoking, go jump in a pool," he recommends. "Your wind is bad, and the smoke seems so nasty when you get out of the water. I just said 'That's it, I'm not smoking anymore,' and I stopped. My swimming improved, and I started lifting weights and biking too. I have friends who are really muscular, but when they get in the pool they can't go anywhere because they smoke.

"My grandmother smoked and got cancer of the vocal cords and died. When I was younger I said a truly smart person doesn't smoke. Now I say, if you want to quit, swim. I haven't had a cigarette for a year."

❖ ❖

Now I'm a fellow with a heart of gold
With the ways of a gentleman I've been told
The kind of a fellow that wouldn't even harm a flea
But if me and a certain character met
The guy that invented the cigarette
I'd murder that son-of-a-gun in the first degree.

Smoke Smoke Smoke that cigarette
Puff Puff Puff and if you smoke yourself to death
They'll tell Peter at the Golden Gate
That you hate to make him wait
But you gotta have another cigarette.
  —*"Smoke! Smoke! Smoke!" by Merle Travis, sung by*
Tex Williams, © 1947 (Renewed) Unichappell Music Inc. &
Elvis Presley Music. All rights administered by Unichappell
Music Inc. All rights reserved. Used by permission.

Patty Young has been a flight attendant for 27 years, and a militant antismoker for the last 23. "An airplane is a locked tube, and anything in the air, you're breathing in, from people's germs to the 43 carcinogens in secondhand smoke. Flight attendants are the victims of pulmonary and cardiovascular rape, hostages at 35,000 feet who can't step outside for a breath of fresh air. Before domestic flights became smokefree, I used to have brown mucus coming out of my nose. The dentist of a girlfriend of mine asked her when she'd started smoking. She'd never smoked, but she had tobacco stains on her teeth.

Flight attendants get sick all the time. We're high cancer risks and walking time bombs. We also suffer from burning eyes, noses, and throats, recurrent sinus and bronchial infections, reduced lung function, chronic fatigue, loss of hearing, and weakened immune systems."

When Young started her campaign against smoking in the air, she stood alone. Even the ACLU told her she had no rights to a smoke-free work environment. "How can I be so damn smart with just two years of college," she retorted, "and all of you so stupid?"

Now she's put together a $5 billion class action suit for flight attendants against all the airlines. At the initial hearing, the tobacco companies showed up with 42 lawyers.

❖   ❖

"I will not stop fighting for our rights as nonsmokers until smoking is banned on every flight that takes off on the face of the earth."

—PATTY YOUNG, *flight attendant*

It is generally clear that people smoke to get nicotine, the

brain-affecting chemical. No nonnicotine smoke has ever caught on, no matter how tasty and sweet-smelling. There's just one puzzle. Why is it that you can fill people up with nicotine through other means—with gum, patches, or intravenously— and they still want to smoke?

Jed E. Rose, who does nicotine research at the Virginia Medical Center, has a theory about this. He has discovered: "Smokers' craving for cigarettes is satisfied more effectively by irritation from smoke in the upper respiratory tract than by nicotine's direct pharmacologic effects on the central nervous system."

When people smoke, they feel the relief as soon as the first puff hits the back of the throat. This happens several seconds before the nicotine reaches the brain. In fact, smokers get satisfaction even when fed low-nicotine smoke, as long as it's harsh on the throat.

Rose concludes that although nicotine is central to smoking, smokers have been so long conditioned to match satisfaction with a smack of smoke in the throat that the upper airway stimulation may even substitute for the effects of nicotine—for an undetermined length of time.

❖ ❖

WITH GOD'S HELP: Saint Blaise of the Throat earned his identification by healing a boy who was choking. On Saint Blaise's Day, Catholics with throat problems can have a special blessing with candles held on each side of the neck.

"I used to reach for a cigarette as soon as I woke in the morning," says Anne Kincaid, "and it was the last thing I did at night, although I was careful never to smoke in bed. Even so, I once fell asleep in the living room and burned a chair.

"I just smoked continually, running through two and a half packs a day. Everything I did went with a cigarette—before, during, and after. I had the idea that I was a person born without willpower, and I didn't think I could quit. But I wanted to. I had become pretty revolted by the habit.

"When I was a child, I had much admired a great-aunt who quit smoking at age 50. I remembered her saying that nothing was less attractive than a grandmother with a cigarette hanging out of her mouth. Age 50 was coming for me. My doctor prescribed nicotine gum, and I stopped on my fiftieth birthday.

"I hardly told anyone that I'd quit because I didn't seriously think I could do it, but the gum helped, and I got through three days. Then someone announced at a big interdepartmental meeting that Anne had quit smoking and let's all give her a big hand. After that, I was too embarrassed to smoke again and never did."

❖   ❖

"Lee Iacocca drives a Chrysler, the chairman of Pepsi drinks Pepsi, the chairman of Nike wears Nikes, but Michael Miles of Philip Morris and Larry Tisch of Loews ... don't use the products they're pushing. They don't smoke any brand."

—JOE CHERNER, *SmokeFree Educational Services*

The tragedy of smoking in un-developed countries is even

more pronounced than it is in the U.S.A. The people in these countries are often not privy to truthful information about smoking, but are currently the targets of big tobacco promotions.

Take a country like Bangladesh, where cigarette consumption is rising. The cost of cigarettes comes directly out of the food budget; for a parent to smoke even five cigarettes a day spells increased dietary deficiencies for the children.

Suppose that parent gets lung cancer. Little medical care is available. The whole family will be employed in looking after the sick person and may well be left destitute afterward. Such societies have many needs, but cigarettes are not among them.

❖ ❖

THE BRIGHTER SIDE: Thanks to encouragement from a Bangladesh health advocacy organization, Bangabhaban, the presidential palace in Bangladesh is now a smoke-free zone.

Death in the West is a documentary showing what really happens to the men who smoke in Marlboro Country. In it, six cowboys dying of lung cancer and emphysema are juxtaposed against Marlboro advertising.

The film appeared once in 1976 on British television, whereupon Philip Morris sued the broadcasting station that showed it and had distribution stopped by court order. It was not until 1982, when Americans for Nonsmokers' Rights (ANR) stepped in, that *Death in the West* was shown on American television.

❖   ❖

Quotes from Death in the West, *distributed by Pyramid Films:*

"I thought that to be a man you had to have a cigarette in your mouth. It took me years to discover that all you really got out of it was lung cancer."

—BOB JULIAN, *age 51, lung cancer*

"I started when I was 17 years old. . . . I wish I knew then what I know now. . . . I have to stop and gasp for breath and it feels like someone has their fingers down in my chest."

—JOHN HOLMES, *age 64, emphysema*

"I started when I was 18 or 19. I wouldn't do it again, I guess. You never get your second chance."

—RAY MADSEN, *age 47, lung cancer*

Young women who don't smoke don't need to worry much about heart attacks. The usual theory is that estrogen provides protection. Young smokers, however, have more to fear. A study published in the *Journal of the American Medical Association* in 1985 compared 555 under-50 women who had survived myocardial infarctions (damage of the heart due to artery blockage) with women hospitalized for other reasons.

The conclusion was that cigarette smoking may account for as many as two-thirds of the heart attacks in women under 50, with the risk rising according to the number of cigarettes smoked daily. Smoking more than 35 cigarettes a day led to seven times the incidence, whereas at 25 to 34 cigarettes a day, the incidence was five times that of a nonsmoker. Smoking was a much higher risk factor than high cholesterol, hypertension, or family history.

❖ ❖

DYING TO SMOKE: According to the American Heart Association, women who smoke and use oral contraceptives are up to 39 times more likely to have heart attacks and up to 22 times more likely to have strokes than women who neither smoke nor use birth control pills.

It's possible that passive smoking creates some problems that active smoking doesn't. Sidestream smoke—the stuff that comes off the burning end of the cigarette—has some substantial differences from mainstream smoke.

Sidestream smoke has a lower temperature and a higher pH. The particles are smaller and much more of the tar evaporates into vapor. When you're breathing sidestream smoke, most of the particles are exhaled (unlike the larger particles of mainstream smoke, which stick temporarily in the lungs). The vapors, however, are absorbed 100 percent into the lungs, from whence they are oxidized and metabolized. They end up in the bloodstream and lymph system. Of course, they are much less concentrated than anything in mainstream smoke.

Most of the tar in mainstream smoke does not stay in the lungs. It lands high in the lungs and then is cleared out as phlegm and ends up being swallowed—which explains the high rate of esophageal cancer among smokers. Passive smokers do not appear to get oral or esophageal cancer, although nasal cancers have been seen. "Once it gets past the nose, sidestream smoke seems to sail straight down into the lungs," says Dr. Judson Wells, an authority on passive smoking.

❖   ❖

A BETTER WORLD: In 1992, a shopping mall in Ellicott City, Maryland, became the first mall in the nation to ban smoking.

"Oh, studies!" says the old smoker. "You can prove any-

thing with studies. Now we've got studies showing vitamin C gives you an extra six years and alcohol is good for you and pet birds cause cancer. Next year, there will be a new bunch of studies. Same with this smoking business. Society's on a vendetta against smoking."

One sees his point, and it's true that you can prove anything with statistics. But there's a difference—namely, that more than 50,000 studies have documented the lethal effects of smoking. Few issues have been so thoroughly researched, and no responsible authority any longer underestimates the dangers of smoking. There's a big difference between this degree of surety and a couple of studies showing that a certain seaweed extends life. Anyone who still imagines that the benefits of smoking may outweigh the drawbacks might also be a candidate for the flat-earth society.

❖   ❖

STUDY OF THE DAY: *In Sweden, a royal order in 1774 required the board of health to investigate unhealthy conditions in certain places in the country. The commission found almost everyone addicted to tobacco ("this dreadful habit"), producing debilitation, sickly offspring, and agricultural waste.*

```
D A Y   2 4 0
```
Nonsmokers rarely get throat (pharyngeal) cancer—unless they are heavy drinkers. Smoking and drinking in some combination cause three-quarters of all throat cancers, but because the two habits so frequently go together, researchers have found it difficult to separate the effects of the two.

However, a study published in *Cancer Research* in 1988 was broad-based enough to conclude that either smoking or drinking alone could cause throat cancer and that the risks multiplied when a person both drank and smoked heavily. For those who smoke two packs and drink four drinks a day, the risk leaps to 35 times the norm for throat and mouth cancers. The risk proved nearly as high for pipe and cigar smokers as for cigarette smokers, but it was lesser (although still high) for smokers of filtered cigarettes. Rates of throat cancer have been increasing among women.

The study showed—after adjusting for alcohol intake—that light and former smokers had a 150 percent greater chance of throat cancer than never-smokers. Smoking between one and two packs a day sent the odds up to 340 percent, and for over two packs a day they went up to 580 percent. Quitting smoking can bring the odds down to those of a never-smoker after ten years—if the person doesn't drink. For drinkers, the risk is greatly reduced, but not eliminated.

"Cigarettes are simultaneously the source of more death and disability than any product ever invented, and also the object of the largest marketing effort ever devoted to any product."

—KENNETH WARNER, PH.D.,
Draft Report, *Tobacco Policy Research Project, 1991*

"I turned down a job once at a university in Georgia," says

art historian Karl Volkmar, "because everyone was smoking cigarettes." A car full of smokers picked him up at the airport, a bunch of smokers took him out to dinner, and then everyone went to someone's house, where they all smoked. "Nobody ever asked me if I minded. The whole art history department smoked. I couldn't take it."

Karl himself was once a five-pack-a-day man. He stopped abruptly, telling himself that he was totally free to do whatever he needed to do to keep from smoking cigarettes—pacing, finger drumming, making faces, going out for walks. "I think smoking is just a plug for physical inactivity. And physical activity dissipates mental distress.

"You're less irritable if you let yourself go physically." The urge to smoke lasted only a few weeks, and the rewards came fast. "Being able to breathe was a novelty. And I liked not having a smelly nicotine-stained mustache and not having crud in my lungs and nose. Plus, from five packs a day, you can save a lot of money by not smoking."

❖   ❖

"Among the minor indecencies of the use of this drug may be mentioned the unwholesome and disgusting odor it imparts to the breath, which in most instances is obvious to a non-tobacco user at several feet distant."
—A. A. WILLIAMS, A Smoker's Pilgrim's Progress, 1922

| D A Y 2 4 2 | "My father-in-law's got cancer and my business is in trouble. Quitting smoking at this point might do me more harm than good." This is a typical speech from one of the millions of smokers who foresees that he will quit someday, but not today.

The flaw in the reasoning is the idea that smoking is delivering a reward. The above forty-year-old smoker remembers how horrible he felt during his several attempts to quit. He never got far enough along to know how much better he would feel now if he hadn't quit quitting. Smoking itself is one of the big stresses in his life. By using smoking to cope with his distress, he not only aggravates his difficulties but misses out on effective strategies for coping.

And yet, we sympathize. "Smoking substitutes for a vacation or for a good night's sleep," he says. To stressed-out smokers, a cigarette represents a little holiday. But in fact, the smoker never gets a real holiday—from the awful burden of smoking. Ex-smokers do have to learn how to relax without smoking. And they do, discovering that real relaxation doesn't raise blood pressure and cholesterol, rob the blood of oxygen, and cause cancer.

LITTLE RELAXATIONS: Exercise. Hot baths. Crossword puzzles. Yoga. Gardening. Lying down. Walking. Sex. Meditating. Toning (see Day 66). Deep breathing. Stretching. Singing. Biofeedback.

You don't have to be a Zen master to be able to shed tension.

| D A Y | 2 4 3 |

Plenty of evidence shows that quite ordinary people can learn to relax even involuntary muscles and to lower their own blood pressure. There are a lot of relaxation methods around. One is biofeedback, which takes training. Charles Stroebel, a doctor who pioneered methods of biofeedback, devised a shortcut for those not requiring intensive work: The Six-Second Relaxation Response.

Here's how: Pause. Think of what you're doing. Relax your jaws. Relax your shoulders. Take a deep breath and as you exhale sense the blood going down to your fingertips. Take another deep breath and feel the blood going down your legs to your toes.

That's it. Do it many times a day. Dr. Stroebel recommends that you choose cues to remind yourself to do it, such as whenever you stop at a red light or hang up the telephone. In time, the relaxation will become automatic and you will maintain yourself in a relaxed state—which both conserves energy and opens the door to pleasure.

A SMOKER'S LIFE: Smoking is a major deterrent to recovery from back pain because the low oxygen levels of smokers prevent lumbar disks from healing. The risk of ending up under the surgeon's knife is tripled if someone with a herniated disk smokes a pack a day or more.

DAY 244

Celebrate your anniversaries. Knowing that if you relapse there will be no cake on that day-to-come is one more incentive to hold fast and true to your resolution. Today is a marker: two-thirds of a year without smoking. Not a five-star anniversary perhaps, but still one worth some self-congratulation. Before long, you'll have a smoke-free year in your pocket.

Take a very deep breath and hold it. Let it out fast. That was a deeper breath than you could take when you were smoking. If you had emphysema, you would have trouble forcing the air out. If you do have emphysema, you would have had more trouble yet if you were still smoking. So be grateful for your 244 days of not smoking.

❖ ❖

"Pop always said he stuck to Chesterfields so that when he got sick he'd know who to sue, but by the time he found out he had emphysema he wasn't well enough to sue."
—BETSEY WANNING HARRIES

In recent years, tobacco com- panies have become ardent defenders of freedom of speech. Philip Morris even cut a $600,000 deal with the National Archives to use the Bill of Rights in its ads. They now invoke Thomas Jefferson and Benjamin Franklin to highlight the injustice of attempts to shut out smoking and cigarette advertising.

Meanwhile, Federal Judge H. Lee Sarokin found in a 1988 case that there was substantial evidence that cigarette companies had engaged in a sophisticated conspiracy "to refute, undermine, and neutralize information coming from the scientific and medical community."

❖ ❖

"Freedom for the tobacco advertiser is the freedom to persuade people to use nicotine, an addictive and dangerous drug. It is quite different from the lack of freedom experienced by most smokers, who want to stop smoking but find after many attempts that they still cannot. It is the freedom to use glossy images to distract from the fact that smoking kills and pollutes. It is freedom to corrupt the language by calling a carcinogenic product 'mild,' and using terms like 'luxury' and 'fresh' to describe it. It is the freedom (and wealth) to attract young people while the health concerns have minimal budgets to counter such words. It is the freedom to make mega-profits while the smoker suffers."

—DR. JUDITH MACKAY,
    director of the Asian Consultancy on Tobacco Control

Education can pay off. Michael Lipsey never became a heavy smoker. He claims that the efforts of his father kept him from ever completely enjoying his cigarettes.

❖ ❖

"My father, who is a radiologist, used to take me to AMA conventions where they had diseased body parts spread out in cases like in a butcher shop. My father always made sure I looked at the cancerous lungs. They were unbelievably horrible. The healthy lungs were mainly flesh-colored and smooth, but the cancerous ones were black and grotesque and covered with growths.

"I grew up and smoked anyhow, and I loved the taste and the sensation of inhaling smoke. But still whenever I smoked, there was always in the back of my mind the fear of what smoking was doing to me and how that very cigarette was taking seven minutes off my life expectancy.

"For years, I bummed cigarettes instead of buying them. A cup of coffee and a Camel and I was in heaven. But I knew that even a couple of cigarettes a day were hurting me. I quit, and though sometimes I still dream about smoking, I don't miss it."

—MICHAEL LIPSEY, *ex-smoker*

In populations with very low
life expectancy, smoking is

not as great a threat to public health as it is in places where
people grow old. If you're fated to die at forty-seven, smoking
may well hasten your end, but you are likely to escape lung
cancer and emphysema.

The United States is presently losing 426,000 of its citizens
a year to smoking, while all of Latin America, with its larger
population, has a smoking-attributable mortality of 98,000.
The latter figure, however, is rising fast. Not only are Latin
Americans smoking more (particularly young people, of whom
there are a great many) but their life expectancies have increased 15 years since 1950. Thus, many in the future will live
long enough to die from smoking.

❖ ❖

*"In any population, the prevalence of smoking and the
demonstrable health effects of tobacco consumption are out
of phase. For some diseases, such as lung cancer, the
lag may be 20 years or more; for heart disease or adverse
outcomes of pregnancy, the lag may be considerably shorter.
But the overall burden of disease reflects the cumulative
long-term impact of tobacco use, or 'maturity' of the
smoking epidemic."*

—U.S. Department of Health and Human Services,
Smoking and Health in the Americas, *1990*

DAY 248   Light smokers have little excuse for smoking. One California study compared light and heavy smokers and found that smoking for heavy smokers was likely to "reflect a maladaptive response to personal and environmental factors." But light smokers mainly smoked socially and were not heavily nicotine dependent.

Although some light smokers still find quitting terribly difficult, smoking is not the glue that holds them together, as it is for some heavy smokers. The problem in quitting for light smokers is more apt to be a failure to take their smoking seriously. They may kid themselves that their habit doesn't really count. They don't think of themselves as real smokers. But they can really die from smokers' diseases.

❖   ❖

THE ODDS: *Smokers of under a pack a day have at least 6 times the risk for lung cancer and 1.72 times the chance of dying prematurely as never-smokers. Smokers of fewer than 15 cigarettes a day have 2.2 times the risk for stroke and 1.3 times the risk for an aortic aneurysm. Even smoking fewer than ten cigarettes a day raises the risk of heart disease to 1.23. Pregnant women who smoke only five cigarettes a day have a significantly greater risk of bearing an unnaturally light baby.*

Most statistics regarding smokers present the increased odds
for getting a disease, but not the likelihood of the disease actually occurring. The savvy smoker when meeting the numbers may well ask: But how great a risk does smoking present overall?

Here are a few facts from the *American Journal of Public Health*. A 35-year-old man who smokes 25 or more cigarettes per day has over a 6 percent chance of dying of lung cancer due to smoking before reaching age 65; the odds for a nonsmoker of the same age are .2 percent. The smoker's chances are 18 percent of dying of lung cancer before age 85.

This 35-year-old heavy smoker also has a 7 percent chance of dying of heart disease due to smoking before age 65. Overall, heavy smokers have a cumulative risk of dying from smoking by age 65 of 16 percent, and the chances that smoking will get them by age 85 are 36 percent. In contrast, a smoker's chances of dying in an auto accident before age 85 are 1 percent.

❖ ❖

Ex-Smoker Odds: A 35-year-old male ex-smoker has a 2 percent chance of dying of lung cancer by age 65 and a 6.5 percent chance before age 85. His chance of dying of heart disease from smoking by age 65 is 1.7 percent; by age 85, it is 5.5 percent.

| D A Y   2 5 0 | More than 5,000 people die annually from cancer of the

esophagus, and three-quarters of these deaths are credited to smoking. The esophagus sustains intense assault from tobacco because most of the particles inhaled by a smoker are eventually coughed up from the upper lungs and then swallowed.

Alcohol can be a contributing factor but mainly at very high levels of consumption. Even light smoking produces a direct risk. An Italian study found that smoking under 15 cigarettes a day doubled the risk of esophageal cancer; the risk for smokers of more than 25 cigarettes a day was 6.2 times that of a non-smoker.

Few people (under 5 percent) get esophageal cancer and live. The only good thing to be said about this brutal disease is that the risk factor drops rapidly after quitting smoking—in three years, it is half that of a current smoker's.

❖ ❖

"Bogie was under the weather in Chicago. He'd always been a cougher ... His explanation was that he'd always had a sensitive throat.

"I was so used to Bogie's cough that I hadn't been aware of any change. He'd been off his food a little, but that wasn't unusual. . . . The doctor found his esophagus a bit inflamed and wanted him to come in for a sputum test in a few days."

[Humphrey Bogart proved to have cancer, and surgeons removed his esophagus. He died ten months later, on January 14, 1957, at age 57.]

—*LAUREN BACALL*, **By Myself,** *1978*

The largest portion of tobacco advertising budgets now goes

to promotion and sponsorship. Such spending could seem fairly harmless—even beneficial—until you realize what the spenders get out of it.

It is no coincidence that most of the events sponsored are sporting events; the sponsor thus gets to associate smoking with its unlikely bedfellows fitness and achievement. An aura of respectability surrounds the brand name that presides over such well-known events as the Virginia Slims Tennis Tournament and the Marlboro Grand Prix. Philip Morris has gone in heavily for high-class cultural events—and so gets its name glossed up at the Metropolitan Opera and New York's Museum of Modern Art.

The special beauty of sponsorship is that the company logo presides over the event. In the Marlboro Grand Prix auto race, the Marlboro logo was on television for 46 minutes. What kid is not going to warm to the name which brings him or her such excitement? Could the company that backs the Matisse Retrospective be all bad?

❖   ❖

TOBACCO POWER: *Olympic diver Greg Louganis testified to Congress that in 1984 he had been eager to become chairperson of the American Cancer Society's Great American Smoke-Out. However, the swimming club where he trained was owned by a subsidiary of Philip Morris. If he accepted the chairmanship, he was told, he would be barred from training with his coach at this club. With the Olympics a few months away, he had no choice but to refuse the honor.*

```
D A Y   2 5 2
```
Alice Giannoccolo lost her vocal cords to cancer. "The worst part," she says, "is when you wake up after a laryngectomy and you can only communicate by writing. And what if no one is there to read your writing?"

After healing, most laryngectomees can use either an electro-larynx or a Blom-Singer Voice Prosthesis. But these aids are far from equal to one's own voice. "You never fully adjust," says Giannoccolo. "You can't talk naturally. You can't laugh. Well, how could I? I can say 'Ha. Ha. Ha.' But I need to use my Blom-Singer Prosthesis even to do that."

Giannoccolo is a leader in the New Voice Group of Marin County, California. "We're getting younger people now," she says. "Two men recently joined, ages 48 and 51. And we're getting more women, the result of more women smoking." Giannoccolo and others from her group visit schools, bringing home to youngsters this less glamorous side of smoking.

"I smoked for about thirty years, off and on," says Giannoccolo. "It was an occupational hazard. I was a psychotherapist and smoked while listening to patients' problems. Back then, smoking wasn't seen as an addiction. Often I was trying to help other people overcome drug addictions, while ignoring my own. There's a great deal of denial in smoking."

❖ ❖

THE ODDS: *Examinations of the vocal cords of 148 male autopsy cases showed that 47 percent of the heavy smokers had precancerous lesions or carcinoma. Only 4.2 percent of nonsmokers had such abnormalities; 12.5 percent of the light smokers had them; and 22.9 percent of the medium smokers. Among ex-smokers, 12.5 percent had precancerous or cancerous lesions.*

In 1981, Pamela Chese- DAY 253

brough joined a gas utility company in Minnesota. By 1986 she had become the supervisor of 16 union dispatchers, all of whom smoked. Pamela had for years been requesting a non-smoking environment; she hated smoke and suffered chronic sore throats from it. But she got no sympathy from her company. In fact, in retaliation for her complaints the dispatchers purposefully kept their cigarettes lit as much as possible. "I wasn't popular," says Pamela. "People didn't even want to be seen talking to me. The union considered smoking a right."

Pamela nonetheless escalated her complaints, and the company fired her. She'd always had good appraisals and steady promotions so she found a lawyer. "My case rested on the Minnesota Clean Air Act and on a letter from my doctor.

"Eventually we settled out of court, and I can't speak of the terms of the agreement. I can say that I bought a new sports car. But the best part was that the week afterwards the company announced a nonsmoking policy that applied to 2,000 people in four states. I'm happy about that but I still look back on it all as a terrible time."

"The amazing thing," says one of Pamela's oldest friends, "is what a quiet unassuming person Pamela always was. But she knew she was right."

❖ ❖

"When a man begins to smoke, he immediately becomes a hog."

—HORACE GREELEY

```
D A Y   2 5 4
```
The subject comes up again and again: "What about Joe Blow and Jane Doe, lifetime smokers, going strong in their eighties?"

It's not impossible for heavy smokers to be walking around at advanced ages. If nothing comes along to knock you dead, you're still alive. Not too many of Blow's or Doe's merry old crowd are likely to be still kicking, but a few were bound to slip by the Grim Reaper. The problem is that Blow and Doe are not the phenomenons they might have been. When they get to the top of the stairs, they have to stop and catch their breaths. People say "Isn't she [he] amazing? Still smoking at that age! And still alive!" But not "Running marathons!" or "Built that new fence last month!"

These people are phenomenons only in the smoking category, not in the age category. They're missing their blue ribbons by smoking. Smoking debilitates. Nobody who smokes is as hardy as he [she] would have been without smoking. The old smokers are easy to spot; they're the wrinkled, rickety-looking ones.

❖   ❖

"It is surprising to what extent men come to regard their habits as necessities: how habit enslaves body and mind; how it perverts the judgment and subsidizes the reason."
—HENRY GIBBONS, M.D., Tobacco and Its Effects, 1868

Elderly people who have smoked for many years may

not believe that quitting will do them much good. They are very wrong. Particularly in regard to cardiovascular problems, their most likely killers, their prospects immediately brighten.

Although smoking may damage some blood vessels irreparably, there is ample evidence that when old people quit smoking, their risk for coronary heart disease declines rapidly. Within one to five years, the risk matches that of never-smokers.

Equally important, old quitters also fast reduce their risks for strokes. In a study reported in the *Journal of American Medicine* in 1985, doctors measured the blood flow in the head ("cerebral perfusion") of elderly volunteers using a noninvasive method. The smokers were shown to have serious reductions in cerebral blood flow—a bad sign, often preceding strokes and dementia.

In this particular study, a group of smokers were analyzed both before and after quitting. A control group of smokers continued smoking. The cerebral blood flow in the quitters steadily improved in just the first year. A separate longitudinal study with many elderly subjects confirmed the fast drop in mortality levels for the quitters.

❖ ❖

"My parents both smoked. My father died of emphysema and then my mother had a series of small strokes, followed by a massive stroke. She spent the last five years of her life in a nursing home, unable to speak, scarcely able to move. I'm sure it was because of smoking."

—BETSEY WANNING HARRIES

| D A Y   2 5 6 | If you're a little heavier than you were when you smoked,

you're average. One of the reasons could be that nicotine increases the metabolic rate. Dr. Kenneth Perkins and colleagues discovered that this metabolic increase, at least in male smokers, becomes particularly great during light exercise.

As smokers are apt to smoke all day, and as they are apt to be doing something while they smoke, this metabolic increase does contribute to holding weight down. So a person who continues to eat the same amount after quitting smoking may gain weight on this basis. However, the actual reduction in calories burned is small enough so that a short daily walk can easily compensate.

Aside from this metabolic churning up, smoking in itself appears to artificially hold down weight. If it's any comfort, you're more likely to be at your God-given weight now than you were as a smoker. If you don't like it, try stepping up a bit the amount of exercise you get and eat healthy foods. Don't diet, which will make you feel deprived, and don't smoke. Much as you might dislike your extra pounds, you still look a lot better than you did gripping a cigarette.

❖   ❖

"To make up for the lost expenditure in calories, I'd recommend very low-level walking, which can be enjoyable. It's not necessary to make your exercise aerobic. Keeping up a demanding exercise program is almost as hard as quitting smoking."

—DR. KENNETH PERKINS,
University of Pittsburgh School of Medicine

Joseph Lamacchia won a court order forbidding his ex-wife to

smoke around his three-year-old son. The boy's constant coughing and wheezing stopped quickly after the air cleared around him. Lamacchia went on to found an organization called Parents Against Secondhand Smoke (PASS, P.O. Box 396, Watertown, MA 02272-0396), which helps parents protect children against smoke—particularly in cases when the other parent is an unrepentant smoker.

In an increasing number of states, secondhand smoke is being taken seriously as an issue in custody cases, particularly when a child has respiratory ailments. In a Tennessee case, the Court of Appeals upheld a decision to award custody of a six-year-old asthmatic boy to the father because the child's mother and grandmother smoked in his presence.

Courts have not yet labeled smoking around children as "child abuse," but the case could certainly be made, particularly if the child has respiratory problems and a physician has already warned a parent against smoking around him/her. Secondhand smoke has an even greater impact on children than on adults because of their less-developed respiratory systems. They also inhale more frequently and absorb more toxins for their weights than grown people.

❖   ❖

"When many of the chemicals in cigarettes are used in the workplace, we require gas masks. But when our children are exposed to them in cigarette smoke, we let them go by."

—JOSEPH LAMACCHIA, *founder of PASS*

In his best-seller, *Aerobics*, Dr. Kenneth Cooper reported on a conditioning program for new recruits in the air force. A thousand young men were divided into five groups: 1) never-smokers; 2) ex-smokers; 3) those who smoked less than 10 cigarettes a day; 4) those who smoked 10 to 30 cigarettes a day; and 5) those who smoked 30 or more.

In a pretest of physical condition, only the never-smokers made it into the "good" category. The ex-smokers were just behind, and the other three groups lined up behind in fairly even order. No one was surprised by this.

What was surprising was the groups' development. "Their progress lines on the chart spread apart the way the peacock on television spreads its tail," wrote Cooper. The 30-plus cigarette group remained a poor fifth, hardly progressing at all and never getting into the "good" category. The others achieved "good," but there was a gap between the under-10-cigarette group and the ex-smokers. The never-smokers remained comfortably in the forefront.

These results are particularly chilling because the men were so young, with few possible years of smoking behind them. Such youthful ex-smokers had lost something they had not gained back. As for the rest: "I can only believe," wrote Cooper, "that as they add years and more cigarette consumption, the performance gap will widen still more."

❖   ❖

"Substantial evidence indicates that tobacco is not addictive. The effects of stopping are no different than those experienced upon discontinuance of any other pleasure."
—THE U.S. CIGARETTE EXPORT, *1988*

One thing you never see in a cigarette ad is an ashtray full

of old butts. Though it's as integral to smoking as nuclear waste is to nuclear power, it's a disgusting sight.

Ex-smokers recurrently say how glad they are to be clean. Cleanliness is foreign to a smoker, as smoking itself is a dirty process. And a smelly one. "There is one way in which tobacco interferes with the sacred relations of domestic life," wrote Dr. Henry Gibbons in 1868. "No neat housekeeper wishes her parlor infected with its stench."

"Our accountant smoked, and when he left," says the office manager of a Washington law firm, "we had a hell of a time making his office habitable again. The whole room was yellow, except behind the pictures. The bookcases were brown, and we had to throw out the Venetian blinds. Other people's offices aren't like that."

Once stale tobacco has penetrated rugs and drapes, it takes months to air out, which is why no-smoking hotel and motel rooms have become poplar. Travelers adamant about not vacationing on smoky mattresses can pick up a copy of *The Nonsmoker's Guide to Bed and Breakfasts,* which lists more than 1,150 places in the U.S., Canada, and Puerto Rico in which smoking is verboten.

❖   ❖

Fact: Consumers' Reports tests window cleaners on windows fouled with cigarette smoke—the hardest grime to remove.

| D A Y   2 6 0 | Many people have thought they'd licked the smoking habit

and found they were wrong. Lady Nicotine is seductive. Eighty years ago, Henry Beach Needham warned quitters of the surprises in store for them.

❖ ❖

"Getting the upper hand of the smoking habit is getting the better of a second self. A confirmed smoker who tries to quit will discover to his surprise that, instead of a single in-good-standing member of society, his hat covers two personalities: one highly respectable and self-respecting, the other a sneak who is capable of a variety of crimes, petty and high; one a Dr. Jeckyll, who, when the cigars are passed, says with a confident gesture, No thank you, I've given up tobacco; the other a Mr. Hyde, who would commit murder, if need be, to obtain a smoke. . . .

"Despite his excessive use of tobacco, this fiend Hyde has a seemingly unending amount of vitality. When you think you have him dead and cremated he springs from his ashes, snatches the tomahawk from the wooden Indian and starts in to raid the cigar store."

—HENRY BEACH NEEDHAM,
Divorcing Lady Nicotine, 1913

In Raynaud's syndrome, blood vessels leading to the fingers

and toes go into spasm (become constricted) for a period lasting for minutes to hours. The fingers and toes tingle, turn white, and are painful. Ulcers may appear, and in advanced cases the extremities can become gangrenous.

The vasoconstriction that causes Raynaud's syndrome is badly exacerbated by smoking. In one test of smokers, a single cigarette produced a marked fall in finger blood flow. It is remarkable that it is possible to find people with Raynaud's syndrome who smoke, because nothing could be worse for the condition, a distinctly unpleasant one, which can lead to gangrene and amputation.

❖ ❖

A SMOKER'S LIFE: One survey discovered that in the face of a smoker, 50 percent of the public will move away from him or her; 39 percent will do nothing; and 4 percent will actually say, "Please put it out."

Caroline S., a divorced mother raising three children and working at a difficult job, smoked a lot. "The more pressure there was the more I smoked," she says. "I worked at a plumbing and heating wholesaler, and people were always screaming at me over the phone. I was smoking two packs a day. I felt pretty horrible.

"Then I got a really severe cold and just stopped smoking cold. I coughed for six months straight after I stopped, clearing out all the mucus in my lungs. Now I feel better than I did when I was twenty years younger. A couple of years ago I went into a new field, insurance, in which I have complete independence.

"I get four weeks' vacation so I've been able to travel, which is what I love. Things have worked out well for me. My ex-husband's new wife even called me up and said 'How did you stand him for so long?'

"When I first stopped, I missed smoking the most when I went to a bar for a drink. I started playing with the little straws on the bar and got some for home as well. I don't even think about smoking anymore. I'd hate for my house to ever again smell the way it used to."

❖ ❖

"Smokers, male and female, inject and excuse idleness in their lives every time they light a cigarette."
—COLETTE *(1873-1954)*

It long has been known that
men who smoke are at high
risk for stroke. The case for women was not so well established
until recently. Not as many studies considered women, and
several that did were too small to be definitive.

But a 1988 study published in the *New England Journal of
Medicine* was both large and thorough. This study followed
118,539 registered nurses, ages 30 to 55, for eight years. Of
these women, 33 percent were smokers.

Even women who smoked only 1 to 14 cigarettes a day
had 2.2 times the number of strokes as nonsmokers. Those
smoking 25 or more cigarettes a day had a risk factor of 3.7.
At 35 to 44 cigarettes a day, the risk was 4.7; for 45 or more
cigarettes a day, the risk rose to 6.2. These results held even
after controlling for other risk factors, such as use of oral contraceptives. A skinny heavy smoker had the highest risk of all.

It is probably because smoking increases blood clotting that
there is such a strong correlation between strokes and smoking.
In the study, quitting smoking proved highly beneficial. For
those who had stopped for more than two years, the risk went
down to 1.4 times that of nonsmokers.

❖   ❖

*"These data suggest that the effect of cigarette smoking on
stroke is due predominantly, if not entirely, to current or
very recent smoking."*

—GRAHAM COLDITZ, ET AL.,
New England Journal of Medicine, *1988*

| D A Y   2 6 4 | If there is one thing clear about quitting smoking, it is that each

quitter has an individual style. Nora Crow, convinced that "good preparation has won more battles than courage," set a date weeks ahead and launched her nonsmoking life equipped with a kit bag of smoking substitutes (toothpicks, lemon drops, rubber bands, and more).

Carol Ule, on the other hand, gave little forethought to the matter. She was a 27-year-old law student when one afternoon halfway through smoking a cigarette, she suddenly said to herself, "This is my last cigarette."

It was. "Mentally, I didn't think of myself as a smoker after that." Ule did have reasons for giving up her two-packs-a-day habit, the main one being that she loved swimming almost as much as she loved smoking, and she knew that her endurance in the water wasn't what it could be.

This was a couple of decades ago, and Ule is grateful that she quit when she did. "Later, it would have been harder with the pressure of the courtroom and the waiting around in the hallways, where many people smoked. Though now nearly all the lawyers have quit. And so have most of our clients."

❖ ❖

"Today you can actually see down the whole corridor. You can actually breathe. It feels great. Your chest doesn't hurt and your eyes don't burn."

—DEPUTY SHERIFF RICK JACKSON,
commenting on the effect of banning smoking at the San Francisco city jail

In addition to all the damage

that smokers in the workplace do to themselves and their offices, their sidestream smoke is a heavy liability. Furthermore, it can precipitate legal problems for the employer.

There are several forms of legal protection for the non-smoker. Under the common-law duty to provide a safe work-place, a tobacco-sensitive employee can go to court to petition for a smoke-free workplace. Under the Occupational Safety and Health Act, employers must eliminate workplace hazards. Workers who have been debilitated by tobacco smoke in the workplace can bring a case under Workmen's Compensation.

❖ ❖

"As an employer concerned with the spiraling cost of health insurance, I cast a jaundiced eye on applicants who smoke. Smokers have more of every kind of illness from colds to cancer. Why should my bottom line profit—which is small enough these days—be sacrificed to an employee's addiction to tobacco? Is there any smoking job seeker who is likely to have skills that a nonsmoker lacks? In this shrinking economy there are plenty of qualified people going after every job. Why should I hire a smoker?"
                                    —MICHAEL LIPSEY, *plumbing contractor*

"I called my mother the other day," said Barbara E., "to tell her some news. She didn't seem much interested, which was strange. I felt hurt and got off the phone. Then I realized that I must have caught her without her cigarettes and so she was pining for a smoke, which she didn't want to mention to me because she knows what I think of her smoking."

Smokers' lives are so wound up in smoking that they don't even notice how distracted they are by their habit. In smoke-free restaurants, it seems natural to them to be concentrating on rushing through the meal so they can get outside and smoke, meanwhile thinking dark thoughts about the companion who ordered dessert. The rest of the time, they hardly think about smoking at all, any more than they think about breathing.

"I smoked for 25 years," says Emil, "and I hardly remember smoking at all. I saw Paris, I sailed in the Caribbean, I got promotions. I guess I was smoking the whole time, but I only have little flickers of remembrances, like the smell of Gauloises. I don't remember my friends' smoking either. I just remember that I thought the ones who *didn't* smoke were odd."

❖   ❖

A Smoker's Life: A two-pack-a-dayer spends three to four hours smoking each day.

Sean Marsee was Athlete of
the Year in 1983 at Oklaho-

ma's Talihina High. In 1984 at age 19, he died of oral cancer. He had begun dipping snuff (wet snuff isn't sniffed but is
held between cheek and gum) at the age of twelve, after getting a free sample at a rodeo—a gift from U.S. Tobacco. He
became a regular user. In high school, a sore in his mouth
proved precancerous. In 1983, he had a third of his tongue
cut out.

But the cancer had metastasized to the lymph nodes, and
further operations and radiation couldn't save him. He was 19
when he died. His mother lost the lawsuit she brought against
U.S. Tobacco.

❖ ❖

*SORRY FACT: The use of snuff is rising among teenage boys.
The majority do not believe that it is particularly harmful.*

| D A Y   2 6 8 | Kaiser Permanente, a giant HMO (health maintenance organization), is making every effort to persuade its members to quit smoking. Such a campaign is not purely for the public good. Because members prepay, the less they use the services, the better for Kaiser.

A Kaiser analysis compared the use of services by elderly smokers and nonsmokers. The conclusion was that smokers and former smokers, who were grouped together, used medical services a lot more than nonsmokers.

Low users averaged 1.38 office visits a year. Of this category, 70 percent had never smoked, and only 30 percent were current or even former smokers. The high users averaged almost 12 visits a year, and 55 percent of them were smokers or former smokers, while 45 percent were never-smokers. Unfortunately, the study did not examine what percentage of current smokers were high users. The percentage would doubtless be high.

The picture of smokers' health shown here is even worse when one considers that the weaker members of the smokers' club were no longer showing up for visits at all, having gone to see their makers. The mean age in this study was 70 years. By age 70, 40 percent of smokers are dead.

❖   ❖

Fact: In 1988, cigarette companies invested $3.27 billion in advertising and promotion, which is more than they spent on wages and nearly as much as they spent on tobacco.

"When you're a pipe smoker,
having your teeth cleaned is

quite an experience," Ben Wootten recalls. "The hygienist
picks away at your gums with those nasty little tools for what
seems like hours. As your gums are usually inflamed from smoking, the pain is notable. Then when they have you rinse and
spit, this black crud comes out, the stuff that was stuck to your
teeth. It's gross. The stuff is the color of oil.

"When you smoke a pipe, you need to have your teeth
cleaned twice as much as normal and it's twice as painful. I
don't think the hygienist necessarily gouges the pipe smokers
on purpose, but I don't imagine he or she really admires the
pipe smokers' mouths, and may not be overly careful. Now
that I've quit smoking, teeth cleaning is surprisingly quick and
painless."

"Any smokers' teeth are frustrating to clean," says Carol
Schatzberg, dental hygienist. "Pipes and cigars leave heavy,
dark stains that are exhausting to work on. I have to do more
scaling and polishing, and sometimes even with the ultrasonic
cleaner I don't have time to get all the stains on the inner sides
off."

❖ ❖

*"If once you get into the way of Smoking, there will be
extreme hazard, of your becoming a Slave to the Pipe, and
ever Insatiably craving for it. People may think what
they will; But such a Slavery is much below the Dignity
of a Rational Creature . . . there can be no Apology for your
taking up the slovenly Practice."*
—COTTON MATHER, **Manaductio Ad Ministerium**, 1726

```
D A Y   2 7 0
```
At nine years old, Jack Ofield started rolling leaves in cigarette papers, which, he says, "burned the tongue and made a kid dizzy." By age 19, living in New York and working in the theater, he was a confirmed pack-a-day smoker of Pall Malls. "I smoked for years," he says, "and what really stopped me was knowing that the tobacco industry was making so much money on this very human addiction. I stopped cold and only missed cigarettes for about six weeks. I kept reaching into my shirt pocket and finding it empty.

"Someone told me to inhale cigars and I'd learn to hate smoking. At the time I was making a film for ABC in Key West, where you could get wonderful Cuban cigars. I didn't inhale and started ordering them by the box. So instead of smoking all day I'd look forward to that one cigar after dinner. It was a much richer experience than cigarettes ever were. I can't remember anything really pleasant about cigarette smoking, but I remember the cigars—and also pipes—with real pleasure. I liked the paraphernalia, the elegant pipes and pretty tins of tobacco, and the ritual. Still, after we moved to California, I bit by bit lost interest and now I haven't lit up anything for a long time."

❖　❖

Tip: Most people who switch from cigarettes to pipes or cigars continue to inhale and so do not improve their health prospects. A few people have found pipes and cigars helpful in exiting from cigarettes, but for most a nicotine patch is a better idea.

Saul Shiffman, Ph.D., studied 263 ex-smokers who were in- structed to call a relapse hot line when they were going through a smoking crisis. The crises were divided up into four clusters: 1) social situations; 2) moments of relaxation, usually at home and often following a meal; 3) work, often at times of anxiety and frustration; and 4) upsetting times, usually at home.

Not all the crises led to smoking, particularly when the subjects called upon coping mechanisms. The mechanisms were divided into behavioral (leaving the scene, drinking water, deep breathing) and cognitive (thinking about the negative effects of smoking, applying willpower) responses. Both kinds of responses seemed equally effective, especially combined.

However, it appeared that people in social situations were least likely to call upon coping mechanisms and most likely to smoke. A follow-up study showed that when people relapsed, they typically returned to regular smoking soon afterward.

❖ ❖

THE BRIGHT SIDE: More and more hotels and motels are providing rooms in which smoking is never allowed, thus sparing nonsmokers the stale tobacco smell that once marked a traveler's nights. A few chains that have made a large percentage of their rooms nonsmoking are Hampton, Homewood Suites, Hilton, Marriott, and the Ritz Carlton. Ask for such a room when you make a reservation.

| D A Y   2 7 2 | "I smoked for twenty years and should have quit eight years before I did," says Wendy Thomas, "because I started getting TIAs [transient ischemic attacks]—an arterial problem.

"I did make efforts and went to a hypnotist who gave me a little mantra that I carried around in my wallet for six years. Finally I quit my job and went up to the mountains for a week. I'd always had a hard time breathing in the mountains so it seemed like a good place to stop. I smoked my last cigarette in the car driving up. Without the usual excuse of pressure at work, I was able to stop smoking for good. It helped that I didn't go back to work for almost a year.

"I didn't really start feeling better until I took up swimming, which I did because a middle-aged friend of mine had begun swimming and had never looked better. At first I'd be trembling after twelve laps, but now I'm good for sixty or seventy."

❖ ❖

"There is an old story of a man who, seeing a bear descending tail foremost from a tree, seized him as a valuable prize. But finding he could not manage the beast he determined to let it go. Immediately, however, the bear clutched the man in his powerful arms, and became master of the situation. So it is with our bad habits."

—HENRY GIBBONS, M.D. Tobacco and Its Effects, 1868

You've now made it through
three-quarters of a year. Nine
months. The gestation and birth period for the human species.
If you don't feel reborn by now, you should at least feel better.
Time to count your blessings.

- You're proud of yourself. Smoking is a hard habit to
  break.
- By every objective test, you're healthier.
- You're most socially desirable.
- You're not setting a bad example to others by smoking.
- You're clean, and so's your house.

And here are the ways in which we hope you have maxi-
mized the joys of quitting.

- You have found new pleasures.
- You have found healthier ways of coping with stress
  than smoking.
- You're more relaxed than when you smoked.
- You deal more directly with problems.
- Not wasting your time smoking, you get more done.
- You're facing reality, drug free.

As a nonsmoker, you should be enjoying a richer life. Often, little steps forward start the process. A little exercise, an occasional evening out, a hot bath, a letter written. And if that
doesn't get you anywhere, go for bigger changes.

❖ ❖

*"When I smoked, I felt like a hamster in a cage. Since I've
quit, I feel 100 percent better."*

—*SALLY T., ex-smoker*

You're in a select group now. Three-quarters of the people who quit on the day you did have relapsed, and most of them are smoking as much as they ever did.

Numerous studies have tried to specify the differences between quitters and relapsers. One such study collected 44 smokers and ex-smokers and ran them through various simulated situations. The group was then graded (by themselves and by judges) for coping skills, stress, and heart rate. The differences between quitters and relapsers were not striking. In negative situations, the relapsers did demonstrate higher stress levels. There were indications that quitters were better at relaxing than relapsers. Quitters had a higher regard for their own social competence than relapsers did, but the judges gave the relapsers higher marks.

Women consistently marked themselves lower in competence and higher in stress than men marked themselves. Women also had higher urges to smoke (no one was allowed to smoke in the course of the testing), which followed perceptions of stress and anxiety.

The study seemed to show that relapsers overreacted to stress. It is important for quitters to remember that there's a big difference between their perceptions of a situation and the actual situation. Most of the circumstances that seem so stressful one day are gone and forgotten the next.

❖   ❖

"Several researchers have reported women to be more likely than men to use smoking to cope with negative affect."
—DAVID A. ABRAMS ET AL., **Health Psychology,** 1987

A memorandum from an un-named Philip Morris lobbyist

fell into the hands of Alan Blum of DOC (Doctors Ought to Care), an antismoking group. The document concerns the management of state legislators. Following are some excerpts:

"In Oklahoma . . . the Industry team is absolutely superb and seems to be able to hold leadership to coming out in the press against cigarette tax every time the governor brings it up, which is often."

"Our new controller [in Texas] . . . will be John Sharp. The plan is to give early and large campaign contributions to Sharp, thereby jumping on the bandwagon early and at the very least buying Sharp's silence when it comes to locating new revenues."

"John Mangum [Arizona] has done a great job with his first session as our lobbyist. He is best friends with the Speaker and used major personal clout to kill our cigarette tax."

"With these people, you get just as much political clout by sponsoring a hunting or fishing trip rather than taking them to NYC. And it's cheaper and less hassle. This group really love to hunt."

❖ ❖

Vox Populi: In November 1992, a ballot proposition passed in Massachusetts to raise the cigarette tax by 26 cents a pack to fund antismoking campaigns. The victory was won despite the $6.9 million spent in opposition by the tobacco industry; proposition supporters spent $520,000.

| D A Y   2 7 6 | Many smokers have seen their mothers and fathers die of smoking diseases, and yet they go on smoking themselves. This bewilders nonsmokers. How can they?

Says Kay V., whose mother died of emphysema: "I've never smoked as much as my mother, and I've always exercised and eaten better foods."

Says Hannah F.: "When my dad died of lung cancer, I actually went back to smoking. I didn't worry about getting cancer myself. I had a general idea that the world was going to be annihilated anyhow so I wouldn't live to be old. Also, I related diseases to the emotional state rather than to the actual cigarettes. I thought if people were in good emotional states they wouldn't get cancer."

One would think, even if one believes this sort of thing, that the fact that someone smoked would be evidence that he or she was not in a superior emotional state and therefore *was* a likely cancer victim. But even in the absence of the "cancer victim" theory, few smokers imagine themselves following in their parents' footsteps in this regard.

❖   ❖

"Only a small portion of people bitten by a rabied animal get rabies, but who would run the risk of a bite because the odds of survival are good?"
—HENRY GIBBONS, M.D., Smoking and Its Effects, 1868

Mrs. Winifred Wootten was never an idle woman, occupy-

ing herself with gardening, golf, tennis, bridge, reading, local charities, and children and grandchildren. As her health and eyes failed, however, her interests dwindled, and she was left with TV and smoking. When her son suggested that smoking might be debilitating, she retorted, "I've got to have some fun, and smoking is the only vice left to me."

If this is the way someone in her seventies feels, there's not much anyone can do about it. But it's not the way you want to live your own old age, and you've taken care of part of the problem by quitting smoking. The other part of the problem is making sure you've got some pleasures in life. If you don't, you're all too likely to end up smoking again. Some people are too duty-bound to indulge themselves in anything they much like, and their lives are grim.

We've said it before, and we'll say it again. Take time, if only ten minutes a day, to do the things that you find uplifting. (This excludes addictive activities, like watching television mindlessly.) If you don't know what such things might be, start looking. We do not suggest living for pleasure alone, but there should be some relief from toil.

❖ ❖

"I got divorced and found it wasn't easy meeting new people in Washington. Especially when you're not invited anywhere on Sundays, which I noticed I wasn't. I decided it was because I smoked so I quit smoking."

—LOUISE P., *ex-smoker*

| D A Y   2 7 8 | While some quitters are too duty-bound and relapse be-

cause smoking is the only kind of fun they know, others are too self-indulgent. The self-indulgent want their fun now. Future oriented they're not. They are incapable of giving up smoking because they can't tolerate discomfort. Or at least they think they can't. In fact, they can.

These people particularly have a lot to gain from quitting. One thing is the evidence that on the other side of self-control there are tremendous rewards. The fun of smoking is not nearly as great as the fun of not smoking. People do many hard things, like climbing Mount Everest, for the exhilaration of the achievement. Quitting smoking is an exhilarating achievement.

Every time you have a bad moment, and still don't smoke, you enter into a higher circle of development. You may not be very comfortable in your new circle, but that's because you've never been there before. The more practice you get, the farther you'll go.

❖   ❖

"Flourishing wits and men of good parts, good fashion, good worth, basely prostitute themselves to every rouge's company, to take Tobacco and drink."
—ROBERT BURTON, **The Anatomy of Melancholy,** *1621*

An added reason that smokers remain vaguely oblivious to

their own peril is that smoking kills so quietly. If someone is murdered or dies in a car crash or takes an overdose, you've got some news. If someone dies of emphysema, the obituary merely remarks that the person died "after a long illness." Thus, the public greatly underestimates the number of people carried away by smoking.

There is also the shadow of doubt as to whether cigarettes alone did the job. This shadow has been given undue influence by the Tobacco Institute, but nonetheless the cause and effect in a smoking death is not as clear as in, say, death by gunshot. A newspaper cannot report, "She died of smoking," if only 98 percent certain that no other factor could be blamed.

Consequently, people often need pointed evidence that they themselves are imperiled. It came to Ann Kidd on holiday at 12,000 feet. She was startled to discover that she could hardly breathe. A short time later she was frightened to wake in the middle of the night very short of breath. The next day she threw her cigarettes into the fireplace and never smoked again. She had failed at quitting many times before. She succeeded when fear got the better of her.

❖   ❖

"For thy sake, Tobacco, I
Would do anything but die."
　　　　　—CHARLES LAMB, A Farewell to Tobacco, 1805

| D A Y   2 8 0 |

Mary Wells, a great singer who was one of Motown's biggest stars in the early sixties, died on July 26, 1992. "My Guy," was her signature song, and she hit the Top Ten charts repeatedly with such songs as "Bye, Bye Baby," "The One Who Really Loves You," and "Two Lovers." After leaving Motown, she continued singing, but her fame declined.

She died at age 49, beaten by a cancer that started in the larynx. She had been a two-pack-a-day smoker. She lost her home before she died, and friends and fans raised money to pay her medical bills.

❖ ❖

"Women often smoke to deal with stress and to suppress anger. Women still aren't supposed to express anger directly, and in today's world, women are frequently under tremendous stress. Most have multiple roles to perform—in jobs and as wives and mothers and helpers—and aren't paid enough to live decently. Men trying to quit smoking tend to relapse in social situations, whereas for women relapse is much more likely to be because of stress."

   —DEBORAH MCCLELLAN,
   International Network for Women Against Tobacco

We know that a mother's smoking causes illness in children.

There's also evidence that smoking contributes to children's intellectual difficulties. Finally comes a study, published in *Pediatrics* in late 1992, concluding that a mother's smoking contributes substantially to children's behavior problems.

This study, conducted by Dr. Michael Weitzman and colleagues, followed 2,256 children between the ages of four and eleven. Parents reported behavior problems according to an index that ranged from antisocial behavior to depression. Mothers who smoked less than a pack a day, through pregnancy and afterward produced children with 1.41 times the chance of extreme behavior problems. Children whose mothers smoked more than a pack a day, but only after pregnancy, were twice as likely to have extreme behavior problems as nonsmokers.

You may immediately think: "But people who smoke are more troubled to begin with, also less educated and poorer, so these problems need not result from smoking per se." The researchers also thought of this and adjusted for the various other problem-makers, such as divorce and low maternal self-esteem, in each child's life. And yet smoking still proved to be a large independent force.

❖   ❖

"I'm not going to tell you that smoking will definitely cause mental health problems in kids. I'm presenting the research. But I would bet on the data. Tobacco is a drug that adults smoke for the effect on the brain so why is it so farfetched that it would do something to the kids' brains as well?"

—MICHAEL WEITZMAN, M.D.

DAY 282 Patty Young saw both parents die of lung cancer. "My parents were beautiful, wonderful people with great integrity. They were much in love. My dad died at 64, and my mother at 68. First Dad got throat cancer. He stopped smoking right then, but just at the five-year point it went into his lungs. My mother continued to smoke and had a nervous breakdown after Dad died and died herself just two years ago.

"These are people who should have had another great twenty years between them. My grandparents lived into their eighties. Everyone has to die sometime, but it can be when the time has come and in a much more predictable way. I truly wish people knew what it is like to die of lung cancer, rotting from the inside out.

"Smoking shouldn't be socially acceptable. Smokers themselves should be leading the protests against this drug addiction. They're the victims. And everyone else is perpetuating the problem by acting as if smoking is normal. Smokers are common drug addicts, and if you love someone who smokes, you should tell them that that's what they are."

❖ ❖

"People ask me why I'm so angry. I say I'm angry because no one else is angry. If someone else would like to be angry for a day, I could take a day off."

—PATTY YOUNG, *antismoking activist*

Gallant efforts are made by researchers to quantify the
amounts of environmental tobacco smoke (ETS) that nonsmokers are exposed to, but the stuff is hard to measure. It would be
impossible to track the thousands of compounds in tobacco
smoke so when researchers test the air, they usually measure for
vapor phase nicotine and respirable suspended particulate
matter (RSP), which fairly accurately reflect smoking levels.

To test the amount of smoke absorbed by nonsmokers,
cotinine—a metabolite of nicotine—is measured in blood, saliva, or urine. Occasionally nonsmokers are found with cotinine
levels similar to those of light smokers, but more typically a nonsmoker's cotinine level approximates 1 percent of a smoker's
level. This seems small, but doesn't tell the whole story as there
are toxic chemicals other than nicotine that weigh much more
heavily in sidestream smoke than in mainstream. For instance,
sidestream smoke emits 31 times more 4-aminobiphenyl, a poison long banned in the dye industry.

A study that measured the levels of cotinine in infants found
large variations even when mothers smoked similar amounts. In
two cases, each mother had smoked 40 cigarettes during the
previous 24 hours, but one baby had a cotinine level 20 times
higher than the other. Closeness, room ventilation, and room
size are important variables. A few babies had levels within
the range of very light smokers.

❖ ❖

*"For every eight smokers the tobacco industry kills, it takes
one nonsmoker with them."*

—STANTON GLANTZ, PH.D.

| D A Y   2 8 4 | If people don't start smoking as teenagers they are highly un-

likely to start later. So keeping kids away from cigarettes is the most important part of any antismoking campaign. The most effective device has proven to be a high tax on cigarettes. Canada steadily increased tobacco taxes throughout the 1980s, and the tax alone now averages about (US) $3. The number of teenagers smoking in Canada has fallen from around 50 percent to 16 percent.

In the U.S.A., teenage smoking remains the most intractable problem. Here, a federal tax of 24 cents is added to state taxes that range from 2.5 cents (Virginia) to 50 cents. Says Garfield Mahood, executive director of Canada's Nonsmokers' Rights Association, "What the U.S. has done is to make tobacco more affordable to kids. If you adjust for inflation, the real price of cigarettes in the U.S. has fallen."

"Canadian tobacco tax levels are not out of line," says Mahood. "Ours are comparable to the rest of the Western world. It's American tobacco tax levels which are out of line."

❖ ❖

"If in the U.S.A. you raised your tobacco taxes over a four-year period to the equivalent of Canada's, you'd anticipate total decline in sales of about 40 percent which would mean about 20 million fewer smokers, which over time would lead to about 6 million fewer smoking deaths and an extra $10 billion per year collected in taxes."

—DAVID SWEANOR,
Nonsmokers' Rights Association of Canada

An unfortunate number of peo-

ple report a return to smoking upon the death of a parent or spouse. There are doubtless profound reasons for wanting to smoke when a family member dies. If that person was a smoker, it may even be a way of identifying with the departed. And a recklessness can overtake one in the face of awful finality. In any event, the death may seem like an awfully good reason to smoke, and the person who reaches for a cigarette at her father's wake may have the thought waft through her mind, "Nobody could blame me for smoking now."

But it's a bad idea anyhow. Cigarettes will not help you get through your grief. Au contraire. To whatever degree you block your grief, you slow your progress through it. If the event is truly overwhelming, you would do much better to get a doctor's prescription for a tranquilizer, which you are much less apt to end up addicted to.

No matter how unexpected death might be, it's one of the things that the ex-smoker should prepare for. The chances are that sooner or later you are going to suffer a harsh loss. Honor the memory of your loved one however else you wish, but don't do it by smoking.

❖   ❖

DYING TO SMOKE: Every cigarette costs the smoker seven minutes of his life, calculates the U.S. Centers for Disease Control. In 1990, Americans lost a total of 5.04 million years of life.

Children with smoking parents are more likely to have asthma and to have it more severely than asthmatic children with non-smoking parents. One study found that asthmatic children exposed to ETS (environmental tobacco smoke) made 50 percent more visits to emergency rooms than those unexposed. In another study, use of asthma medication was more frequent when the mothers smoked more than ten cigarettes a day.

Michael Weitzman, M.D., and colleagues studied 4,331 children up to five years old. Odds of having asthma were 2.1 times as high when mothers smoked more than ten cigarettes a day. Another study of children in Tucson whose mothers had less than a twelfth-grade education found 250 percent more cases of asthma among those children whose mothers smoked more than ten cigarettes a day.

Says Dr. Weitzman, "The single most potent thing that parents can do to prevent their kids from having asthma is to not smoke."

❖   ❖

"I suffered terribly from asthma as a child and was always being rushed to the emergency ward. I'm sure it had a lot to do with the fact that both my parents smoked like chimneys. My father was a long-distance truck driver and was away a lot, but my mother was home smoking all the time. Everyone thought it was remarkable that my asthma cleared up when I left home, but I'm not sure it was so remarkable."

—CAROLYN B., nonsmoker

If you were to smoke a cigarette while having an angio-

gram, the evidence would be right there on your X rays. Your coronary arteries would contract. This contraction lessens the supply of blood to the heart and, in people with heart problems, can lead to attacks of angina pectoris.

Angina is chest pain caused by too little blood (and, consequently, oxygen) reaching the heart. People with angina are at high risk for heart attacks, and smokers have a twentyfold risk of suffering from angina produced by spasms.

Even secondhand smoke is sufficient to bring on attacks of angina in a person who is exercising. On exertion, the heart demands extra blood; polluted air decreases the chance of the heart receiving it.

❖ ❖

THE ODDS: *During the course of a 13-year study of smokers who had suffered heart attacks or unstable angina, 82 percent of those who continued to smoke died. Of those who quit smoking, only 37 percent died.*

| D A Y   2 8 8 | Today it seems hard to believe that a cigarette maker once would advertise "More doctors smoke Camels." Now a doctor's main interest in smoking is in getting her patients to stop. A few years ago a doctor would say to a patient, "Well, you know it's bad for you," and move on to other things. There was some feeling that it was not the doctor's business to advise on life-style changes.

Your doctor is now under pressure to go after her smoking patients. There has been a recognition that some people indeed listen to their doctors, rather better than they listen to their husbands or wives or parents or children, and the doctor who doesn't take advantage of her authority is negligent. After all, there's little else she can do for her patients that would do them more good.

The National Cancer Institute is making a big push to enlist doctors to the front lines of the quitting campaign. A number of experimental trials have produced data showing which are the most effective techniques for doctors to use, and doctors come to their new roles equipped with game plans, teaching materials, and even sometimes course work. What the smoker is apt to hear from his doctor these days is, "Why don't we set a quit date right now?"

❖   ❖

My theme's the Weed, the filthy, fetid weed,
So ye who smoke, or chew, or snuff, take heed,
For I have nibb'd my quill anew,
And here give notice that I'm after you."

—HENRY SHULTS, 1857

Because breast cancer seems

to be on the rise, at least in younger women, the smoking/breast cancer connection has been examined extensively. To date, a correlation has not been established. However, there is a new line of investigation afoot, associating breast cancer with passive smoking.

A study by Dr. T. Hirayama, a distinguished researcher in Japan, discovered that nonsmoking women whose husbands smoked had a higher risk of breast cancer than women with nonsmoking husbands. This was particularly true among younger women, as was borne out in a similar study in North Carolina by Dr. Dale Sandler.

It may be that past studies have not shown increased breast cancer odds for active smokers because many of the baseline group, nonsmokers, were actually passive smokers—and thus themselves had higher odds for breast cancer. When smokers are compared with never-exposed nonsmokers, the smokers' odds for breast cancer are increased. All active smokers are, of course, also passive smokers. More and larger studies are needed.

❖ ❖

"A . . . possibility is that most of the breast carcinogenic damage may be coming from the vapor phase constituent in the cigarette smoke. Recent evidence indicates that 70% of the tar in environmental tobacco smoke is in the vapor phase, whereas all of the tar in direct smoking is in the particulate phase. Particulate phase smoke tends to be cleared into the mouth and swallowed, while vapor phase constituents absorb into the blood and lymph systems."

—A. JUDSON WELLS, PH.D.,
letter to the American Journal of Epidemiology, *1991*

"I tried to quit over and over," says Julie Smith, "and though I finally got my intake down to about half a pack a day, smoking still made me feel terrible. My chest and throat hurt and my lungs ached, and yet I loved smoking. I especially loved the way it would rev me up; of course, I mostly needed revving up because I was draggy from smoking.

"I tried everything to quit, including a self-hypnosis tape, which I would fall asleep listening to at night. I really liked the tape, especially when it said, 'You are a nonsmoker. You walk into a room full of people smoking, and you feel perfectly comfortable, and you don't want to smoke.' I'd think 'I'd give anything to feel that way!' But I didn't do the one thing the tape said—set a date to quit smoking.

"So as the tape wasn't working, I put it away. Then New Year's Eve came and I made my resolution to quit smoking the way I had every New Year's Eve. And to my tremendous surprise, when I woke up I didn't want to smoke. I haven't wanted to smoke since. I had the easiest time quitting of anyone I know, and I absolutely credit the tape, though I can't imagine my method would work for anyone else."

❖   ❖

"The day I quit I felt instantly much better. I wish I could convey to smokers how wonderful not smoking is. Not only do my throat and chest not hurt, I don't have to live with that ambivalence about smoking anymore—do I want to smoke or not?—loving the cigarette and hating how it made me feel. I don't want to smoke now, and I'd be terrified to try."

—JULIE SMITH, ex-smoker

Many research dollars have gone to studying the quit-

smoking process. The great hope is for someone to figure out why it is some people stop smoking forever and others stop and then smoke again. Relapse is the Achilles' heel of the smoking cessation business. Short-term stopping is no great trick.

Despite all the effort, nobody has found the grand determinant of relapse. Human beings remain infinitely various, and no one can yet predict, or prevent, relapses. But rather than conclude that the outcome is controlled by the stars above, we continue to ponder and try to learn from what clues we have.

Research shows that should you smoke a single cigarette, it is not a good idea to feel guilty about it. Do not leap to the conclusion that you are a weak, inferior person who will never quit smoking. And most important, do not smoke another cigarette. Better you shouldn't even finish the one you started. If you failed to enlist what the professionals call "cognitive or behavioral coping strategies" before you started to smoke, call on them now.

❖   ❖

IMMEDIATELY AFTER RELAPSE: Get rid of cigarettes. Take a walk. Indulge yourself in something other than smoking. Put a rubber band around your waist and snap it when you want to smoke. Remind yourself of why you quit smoking. Consider the situation that led you to smoke—how can you avoid a recurrence? By now, you know many other techniques for not smoking. Bring them forward. If you don't go on to a second cigarette, you'll be all right.

| D A Y   2 9 2 | "I smoked a total of 11 years over a period of 18 years,"

says Ralph Howard Hill. "Sometimes I'd quit for three months or six months; once I quit for two and a half years. Then some anxiety would come up, and I'd be smoking two packs a day again."

Seventeen years ago he successfully quit. "I was scared. I knew if I didn't stop, smoking would kill me. I decided that I could do anything I wanted except smoke: Get drunk. Not work. Make a fool of myself. I tried to break down every aspect of smoking and find a substitute for it. I carried around a baby bottle in my backpack with brandy or grapefruit in it. That took care of the sucking and also the need for a jolt in the back of the throat. I chewed filtered cigarette holders. They were good for gesturing with too. I kept a supply of fresh peas on hand. I took a deep breath whenever I wanted a cigarette.

"Some people just tough it out, but I realized that wasn't for me. I even had a round of hypnosis before quitting. One of the key things keeping me going was the knowledge that after ten years, the life expectancy of an ex-smoker equals that of a non-smoker. Not only do you get a longer life, you get more done. I've written 13 books since I quit. I wrote zero before."

❖   ❖

A SMOKER'S LIFE: Two-pack-a-day smokers suffer their first heart attacks at an average age of 51.

Smokers are often restless, even fidgety, people. And so are ex-smokers. There's no disgrace in this. The tasks of modern life more often than not involve only one aspect of our beings. It may be the brain and not the body (the accountant) or the body without the brain (the chicken plucker) or the voice stripped of emotions (the reservations clerk). The cigarette helps to deaden the cries of anguish from the soul.

These cries don't only come from ex-smokers. Plenty of non-smokers fidget too. "I met a woman in a waiting room who also had rubber bands around her wrists," said Nora Crow. "I said, 'You must be giving up smoking too!' 'Oh, no,' she answered, 'I always wear these so as to have something to fiddle with.'"

It's obvious why so many smokers think talking on the telephone demands a cigarette. A telephone conversation leaves out many elements of normal interchange—facial expression, gestures, mobility. The Chinese Iron Balls (mentioned in Day 81) are not only a satisfactory diversion, they supposedly stimulate acupuncture points, thus (according to the brochure) "relieving your fatigue, drowning your worries, and, moreover, prolonging your life."

Then, there's exercise. The construction worker who does yoga stretches in his break will return to work more content than the one who smokes a cigarette. Exercise isn't only for the sedentary.

❖   ❖

"Television convinced us that you could smoke all the time. Before that, it was something that you were more apt to do just now and then."

—RUBY MORRIS, *ex-smoker*

| D A Y   2 9 4 | Now that you're an ex-smoker and likely to remain one, the question comes up of whether to hassle your still-smoking friends.

There are two aspects of this question. One is whether someone else's smoke truly bothers you, or even worse, tempts you. If it does, the only reason you would tolerate it is an extraordinary desire to be ingratiating.

The second question is how accommodating you wish to be to a smoker. Since smoking became unpopular, many people who think they don't care about dying have been intimidated into quitting, and this must be regarded as a good thing. So, while the smell of smoke may not be fiercely repellent to you, kindness to smokers is not a particularly good cause.

A few smokers respond to rejection by smoking more, but these are the minority. Most of us want to be in the social mainstream. We took up smoking as teenagers to be as cool as our friends, and now that all our friends have quit, to stay cool we'll have to quit, too. When a community tilts toward nonsmoking, there comes a great surge of quitting. So while there's no benefit in being condescending toward smokers, there's no need to encourage them. Embarrassment is a strong motivator.

❖　❖

"I quit because the people around me became intolerable."
　　　　　　　　　　　　　　　—HELENA W., ex-smoker

Smokers aren't the best risks behind the wheel. A study in

Massachusetts found that they are more likely to speed, they run more red lights, and they get in more accidents than non-smokers.

Perhaps this isn't so surprising, as the profile of a smoker is of a risk-taking personality. In the study, the smokers got 46 percent more traffic tickets and were involved in 50 percent more accidents. This wasn't because smokers are younger and drink more. Even adjusting for age and drink habits, smokers got into more than their share of accidents. Many auto insurance policies offer reduced rates for nonsmokers.

"Smokers get 50 percent more speeding tickets, and smoking doesn't make you speed, so it's probably the risk-taking personality more than the smoking in itself that raises accident statistics among smokers," says Dr. Joseph DiFranza, who did the study. "However, just after the study came out, we got a woman in the emergency room with a concussion. She'd dropped her cigarette and had driven into a telephone pole while she was trying to find it. We've heard many descriptions of burning embers knocked off by the steering wheel and falling into someone's lap, followed by a collision."

❖   ❖

"I couldn't make the argument that quitting smoking in itself is going to drastically reduce your chances of being in an accident. But after quitting smoking, many people start to take better care of themselves in other ways, such as doing up their seat belts and driving more carefully."
—JOSEPH DiFRANZA, M.D.,
University of Massachusetts Medical Center

| D A Y   2 9 6 | The importance of discourag-
ing children from smoking can-
not be exaggerated. Not only because, once started, they are
likely to have a terrible time in stopping, but because the younger one is at starting, the greater the risk of permanent damage
to the lungs and bronchial tubes.

❖   ❖

"I have abstained from cigarettes for 23 years, more than
double the time one should stop in order to achieve the
mortality rate of lifelong nonsmokers, and therefore I
have reason to believe, or hope, that in terms of lung
cancer and heart disease I bailed out in time. Yet although
the attacks of bronchitis are not nearly so virulent and
debilitating as they were when I was still a smoker, they
do come back with chronic, often exhausting persistence,
casting a somber cloud over all my winters. I trace their
origin to that first long and thrilling drag I took from a
Philip Morris at the age of 14."

—WILLIAM STYRON, The Nation, 1987

The Environmental Protection Agency (EPA) in 1991 re-

leased a draft report on secondhand smoke that concludes that passive smoking kills 37,000 Americans a year through heart disease. The report was written by various authorities; and two respected researchers, Dr. Stanton Glantz and Dr. William Parmley, of the University of California at San Francisco, wrote the section on heart disease.

The study was never formally released. Why not? Because it is controversial, although not in the eyes of the medical establishment or to the public at large. The objections to the report, vociferous on the subject of death rates, have come from the Council for Tobacco Research, which is a creation of the tobacco industry.

"The work in question was very thoroughly reviewed by the EPA and others," said Dr. Glantz. "The death estimates follow from textbook epidemiological arithmetic. The only reviewers who raised any serious criticism of the work were from the Council for Tobacco Research."

❖   ❖

"There's a forest full of data that says tobacco kills people, and sitting on one tree is a lizard with a different biochemical and physiological makeup. The [tobacco] industry focuses on that lizard—that tiny bit of marginal evidence."

—Dr. Anthony Colucci, *onetime top researcher for R. J. Reynolds and now industry critic,* **The Wall Street Journal,** *February 11, 1993*

The Reverend Melvin Tuggle is responsible for souls at the Garden of Prayer Baptist Church in East Baltimore, Maryland, a parish intimately acquainted with crime, drugs, and AIDS. But, says Reverend Tuggle, "If I have one goal in life other than preaching the Gospel, that's to fight the tobacco industry.

"I could not see my people smoking and killing themselves and tell them they were going to heaven. The community is dying faster from cigarettes than from anything else.

"For years, the church winked at smoking. But the word of God is clear: your body is the temple of the Holy Spirit. You can't put poison in it and be a Christian. Smoking is a sin."

Reverend Tuggle has been preaching against smoking for a long time—with results. In his congregation of 250 to 300 people, only about 10 still smoke. The Garden of Prayer Church runs quitting classes for the community, and Reverend Tuggle is now spearheading a high-blitz campaign, Project Bless, that will tackle the tobacco industry. Tobacco companies give enormous amounts of money to black politicians, charities, and media. Project Bless will spotlight the death and destruction this money buys.

❖   ❖

"I don't think it's complicated getting people to turn against smoking. You have to find out what means more to them than anything else. Most people will overcome any addiction once they realize this is what's at stake."

—THE REVEREND MELVIN TUGGLE

If the tobacco industry just qui-

etly sold cigarettes to people who wanted them, one wouldn't mind them so much. But they have fought tooth and nail against every smoking ordinance they could catch up with. And they have fought dirty.

It is a favorite theme of the tobacco industry that when towns ban smoking in restaurants, restaurants lose business. The tobacco industry funds Restaurants for a Sensible Voluntary Policy (RSVP), which analyzes smoking bans and always discovers that business drops off 30 percent after the ban. This gets local restaurants mighty scared.

However, the methodology for the RSVP studies is wildly irregular. Stanton Glantz and Lisa Smith of the University of California analyzed restaurant sales tax receipts for eight California cities and concluded: "If anything, 100 percent smoke-free restaurant ordinances make restaurants more competitive for retail sales dollars."

❖ ❖

"Three years ago I fought very hard to defeat the Beverly Hills no-smoking ordinance ... [which we did] with major funding from the tobacco industry. But times have changed. Ten months ago I made all four of my restaurants 100 percent no smoking. [Despite the economy], Jacopo's sales are about the same as last year.... Guests tell me every day that they love our smoke-free dining and Jacopo's great food."

—BARRY FOGEL, *restaurant owner, Beverly Hills, 1992*

| D A Y   3 0 0 | The American Cancer Society is working on a study of 1.2 million men and women. The results are not yet official, but the indications are that mortality risks among smokers have increased substantially for most of the eight major cancer sites causally linked with cigarette smoking.

When the final tally is in, it is expected that smoking will be credited for 157,000 cancer deaths in 1991—a third of all cancer deaths. At the moment, smoking appears to contribute to 21 percent of women's cancer deaths and to 45 percent of cancer deaths in men. However, the women's share of cancer has been steadily increasing in our era. Among all smokers, lung cancer apparently has now replaced coronary heart disease as the leading cause of excess mortality.

❖ ❖

"No oncologist can ever talk about lung cancer without turning blue in the face. It is just such an incredible tragedy when you think of the number of people who die every year needlessly, needlessly because of cigarette smoking."
—STEVEN A. ROSENBERG, *Chief of Surgery, National Cancer Institute*

Miki McCaslin made her plan months in advance to quit

smoking on her thirtieth birthday. Although her husband-to-be was not yet in sight she had a vision of home and family, and she did not want it to include cigarettes. Miki's mother had quit smoking when she caught herself diapering her first baby with a cigarette hanging out of her mouth. "Disgusting," her mother called it years later, and little Miki remembered.

Miki was nonetheless grateful that her parents, who came to visit for the weekend of her birthday, did not comment on either her intensely heavy smoking the day before her birthday or on her not smoking the following day. Her father had quit two years earlier when his doctor had laid down an ultimatum: Quit or find a new doctor. Miki herself had quit for a year once herself but when she gained a considerable amount of weight, she reverted to smoking.

"I discovered from that first time that smoking again wouldn't make me lose weight and that if I tried to have just one cigarette instead of dessert I'd soon be smoking a carton a week again. I did gain weight, and I still weigh more than I'd like to, but I would even if I were smoking. At least I'm healthy."

❖ ❖

"I've got three strong, healthy children, and I'm terribly glad I quit smoking before I first became pregnant and that my children aren't growing up around cigarettes."
—MIKI MCCASLIN, *ex-smoker*

Tobacco is a drug, but its intoxication level is so slight that no one thinks of smokers as being under the influence. No one, that is, except Leo Tolstoy, who believed that people should strive for the highest consciousness. Even the scarcely perceptible effects of tobacco, he felt, had significant consequences.

❖ ❖

"But is it possible that such a small, such a tiny change as a slight intoxication, produced by a moderate use of wine and tobacco, can produce any important consequences? Of course, if a man fills himself with opium or hashish, or with wine, so that he falls and loses his reason, the consequences of such an intoxication may be very serious; but a man's being under a very slight influence of liquor or tobacco can in no way have any serious consequences, people generally say. It seems to people that a slight intoxication, a slight dimming of one's conscience, cannot produce any serious results. But to think thus is the same as to think that it may hurt a watch to strike it against the stone, but that sand getting to the middle of its mechanism cannot hurt it."

—LEO TOLSTOY, Why People Become Intoxicated, 1890

In 1938, Raymond Pearl published an article in *Science*
magazine that should have wrapped up the smoking question
then and there. In it, he reported on the age at death of 6,813
men—nonsmokers, moderate smokers, and heavy smokers. As
we would predict today, the smokers dropped off much faster
than the nonsmokers, and the heavy smokers fastest of all.

It is outrageous that in all the years since Pearl's work, it has
been found necessary to torture countless animals, interview
millions of mourners, and fund thousands of laboratories—all to
resolve a question that was resolved by Pearl. Alas, the epidemic of smoking was less than halfway to its peak in 1938,
and women had only begun to join it. Millions of lives could
have been saved if strong government action had been taken
then. We have been fiddling while Rome burned.

❖   ❖

*"I quit smoking for about the tenth time on January 1, 1965.
I was smoking about two packs a day and had been trying
to quit for two years ... ever since a doctor in Italy
showed me an X ray of my lungs, ranting, 'Morte,
morte,' to make me understand what I was doing to my
body."*

—LARRY HAGMAN, *actor, ex-smoker*

| D A Y   3 0 4 | Smokers lose their voices in varying degrees. "The changes are most pronounced in women," says Robin Rossman, a speech pathologist who has worked with many ex-smokers trying to recover their voices. "Tobacco smoke irritates the vocal cords, which causes them to swell, and swollen vocal cords produce a lower huskier pitch. If you smoke long enough, you may end up with what is called a 'smoker's voice'—permanently low-pitched and raspy."

Nodules, common on smokers' vocal cords, also interfere with voice production. In nightclub circles a husky female voice was once thought sexy, but such a voice hasn't got staying power and its range of expression is limited.

A professional voice user—actor, singer, political candidate—is particularly susceptible to small changes in the vocal cords, says Rossman. Singers have problems just from the secondhand smoke in clubs. "Smoking and alcohol are a particularly deadly combination," Rossman notes. "Alcohol causes general dehydration and people when drinking are apt to abuse their voices." Anyone who had the shock of hearing Judy Garland sing in the later part of her short life heard an example of this destruction.

❖ ❖

"We can facilitate the return of a normal voice after someone has stopped smoking, but the higher registers may be gone for good."

—ROBIN ROSSMAN, *M.A., C.C.C., speech pathologist*

Deborah D. started smoking at 13 and regretted it by the time

she was 16, when she found she couldn't stop. At 21, she quit, but nine months later started again. "I was depressed and out of work, and people around me were smoking."

Over the next 14 years, she tried most of the available strategies. Hypnotherapy didn't work and cutting down wasn't for her. Finally, she tried acupuncture. "The acupuncturist explained that the concept is to soothe the nerves that create the addictive desire. I had about eight treatments and haven't smoked since."

Not that it was easy. Knowing that drinking led to smoking, Deborah went to AA meetings, didn't drink for three months, and applied the AA concept to smoking. "I quit one day at a time. Even after the craving wears off, the habit lingers. I still reach for a cigarette while I'm putting on my mascara in the morning.

"Still, I'm very pleased to have quit. I feel good. I don't get asthma attacks in the spring anymore. I'm tasting and smelling things more. [An especially good thing, as Deborah is a chef and restaurant owner.] I really wanted to clean up my life, get it under control, and smoking was a big issue."

❖   ❖

"At times I am simply enveloped in a cloud of longing for a cigarette, which then quickly lifts, like a fog. I don't succumb because I know one cigarette would never satisfy me. The craving only lasts five minutes and then I forget all about it for weeks."

—DEBORAH D., *ex-smoker*

```
D A Y   3 0 6
```
Benzene, which is released by petroleum refining, is a known cause of leukemia. People worry about exposure from the air in industrial areas, but a long-term EPA study found that by far the greatest exposure to benzene is self-inflicted—from cigarettes.

"The average smoker takes in about 1.8 mg. of benzene per day, nearly ten times the average daily intake for nonsmokers," reported Lance Wallace, a scientist at the EPA. "In typical homes of smokers, benzene levels on average are 50 percent higher than in homes of nonsmokers."

Smoking may be causing some 14 percent of all leukemias, says Ross Brownson, the lead author of a 1993 report that analyzes 15 studies done over the past twenty years. The most strongly affected type of leukemia is AML (acute myeloid leukemia), a common type which shows up 40 percent more in smokers than in nonsmokers. For all leukemias, the smoker's risk is 40 percent greater; for smokers of over a pack a day, the risk rises to 60 percent greater.

Smokers also have higher rates of myeloma, a tumor of the bone marrow. Tobacco smoke contains radioactive substances as well as benzene, which may be actors in inducing malignancies in bone marrow and in white blood cells.

THE CASUALTY LIST: *A study of mortality among 248,000 veterans found leukemia the cause of death for 723 of them. The odds for leukemia were 50 percent higher for smokers than for nonsmokers, and rose with the amount smoked.*

Once a company has banned smoking on the premises, the

next step is to refuse to hire smokers. Although it is illegal to discriminate on grounds of race, sex, age, and handicap, antidiscrimination suits by smokers have been mainly unsuccessful. (However, "smokers' rights" bills have passed in over half our states—entirely through pressure on legislatures by tobacco lobbyists—with the intention of forcing employers to hire smokers. The legitimacy of these bills has not been determined by the courts.)

Meanwhile, in other states employers can legally bypass smokers. Financially, it is greatly to an employers' benefit to hire nonsmokers, although the employer with such a policy risks lawsuits. Smokers claim invasion of privacy as well as discrimination.

Companies launching no-smoker policies usually grandfather in present employees, while financing quitting programs for the smokers. Although so far only about 6 percent of American companies have moved so definitely against smoking, the number is rising. Fire and police departments have been in the forefront because local tax bases have been seriously drained by high rates of disability paid out to smoking officers.

❖ ❖

A Smoker's Life: One smoker brought a suit against a company with the claim that as a tobacco addict she was a handicapped worker. The court ruled that her "handicap" was correctible, and the suit was dismissed.

Two additional sites for cancer
in smokers are the renal pelvis
and ureter (The "renal pelvis" is the funnellike end of the kidney
leading into the ureter.) A study published in the *Journal of the
American Medical Association* in 1992 revealed that a smoker
bears a 3.1 increase in risk for cancer in these sites. Those
with more than 45 years of smoking behind them carry a
7.2-fold increased risk. For those who quit smoking, the risk decreased.

The study concluded that seven of ten cancers of the renal
pelvis in men and almost four of ten in women are a result of
smoking. With the elimination of smoking, these would become rare cancers.

❖ ❖

*EARLY GRAVE: The author John Cheever, considered by many
the best short-story writer of our time, smoked for fifty years,
quitting shortly after winning the Pulitzer Prize for
fiction in 1979. Post-quitting, he was delighted to find
himself easily sailing up hills on his bicycle. He was also
gratified by the wonderful taste restored to his food.*

*Alas, these pleasures did not last long. In 1981 he
was diagnosed with cancer of the kidney, which appeared
to have begun in the renal pelvis. He died a year later, age
70.*

In 1990, California voters passed a ballot proposition

that taxed cigarettes an extra 25 cents per pack to fund antismoking education and research. The program has had a noticeable impact, and the number of smokers in California is declining fast.

This is what happens when the will of the people prevails. California propositions face each voter on the ballot and so bypass the legislature. The tobacco surtax passed despite heavy advertising against it by the tobacco industry.

In Sacramento, the state capital, tobacco industry money calls the tune and the will of the people does not prevail. Numerous antismoking bills went down in flames while the California Assembly Speaker, Willie Brown, was collecting $128,000 from tobacco interests for his 1992 campaign. Besides campaign contributions, during the 1992 legislative session, tobacco interests invested $2 million in well-connected lobbyists. Thanks to some of the lobbyists' spunkier efforts, a smokers' rights bill reached the governor's desk.

"They [tobacco interests] have inexhaustible resources, and they have a small agenda with one motive: to sell the maximum numbers of cigarettes in the state of California and to kill anything that inhibits that," says retiring Assemblyman Lloyd Connelly, who fought the tobacco interests without success.

❖ ❖

Tobacco Power: Tobacco companies also endear themselves to key legislators by making numerous contributions to charities in the legislators' districts. This way the companies can buy influence without the limitations imposed by campaign finance laws.

One of the best parts of becoming a nonsmoker is the
shedding of guilt. In this day and age, to smoke and not feel
guilty requires a rhinoceros skin. It was bad enough when you
only knew you were killing yourself. Now that secondhand
smoke has proven deadly, any decent conscience is heavy indeed.

Besides the sickness and death business, there was the filth-
iness of the habit. And then you knew, at least in the back of
your mind, that you weren't facing life straight on. Smoking is
something like an illicit affair: it takes up a lot of time and energy, but you'd rather that no one knew about it.

The less popular smoking became, the more alienated you
became when you were a smoker. When people glared at
you, it killed some of the pleasure in smoking, no matter how
defensive you appeared. It was really nicer when everyone just
went away and left you alone with your cigarettes. But some
families wouldn't go away, and neither would the guilt—until
you stopped smoking.

❖   ❖

*"Cigarettes were a metaphor for how I formed relationships.
I felt in all of them that I had to inhale a certain amount
of poison. After I stopped poisoning myself with
cigarettes, I stopped putting up with abuse from other
people."*

—JEANNE R., *ex-smoker*

North Carolina has the second highest infant mortality rate in

the country, so it was praiseworthy for a coalition of state agencies to launch a campaign to educate future mothers. What outraged health advocates was that none of the brochures and posters produced said a word about smoking.

The published materials emphasized the risks attached to alcohol, cocaine, and other illegal drugs, as well as those from cold medicine and aspirin. The content was overseen by the state's lieutenant governor, James C. Gardner. According to a spokesperson for Gardner, the campaign was intended to target illegal drugs; references to smoking "might have diluted the message." The spokesperson also expressed doubt that the state's General Assembly would have provided the funding for the campaign if it had included an antitobacco message.

North Carolina is the top tobacco-growing state in the nation, and more than 28 percent of the women of reproductive age in the state smoke. Gardner plans to run for governor.

❖ ❖

"Smoking is probably the most important modifiable cause of poor pregnancy outcome among women in the United States."

—ANTONIA NOVELLO, U.S. Surgeon General

| D A Y   3 1 2 | Tobacco price supports do not actually cost taxpayers much

because they are maintained primarily by the tobacco industry. There is even an argument that because price supports keep the price of tobacco high, they are beneficial. However, you may be surprised to learn a couple of the ways in which your tax dollars fund smoking.

- The Department of Agriculture gave $3.36 million to Tobacco Associates (a group of U.S. tobacco growers) to use in helping government-owned cigarette monopolies abroad make a blended cigarette with American tobacco. The object is to enlarge the market for American tobacco.
- In 1992, the White House approved $850,000 for tobacco production equipment in Turkey. According to an internal Department of Agriculture memorandum, the funds were part of the compensation for Turkey's participation in the Gulf War. The General Accounting Office is reviewing the legality of the expenditure.

❖ ❖

"The support of politicians and political parties by those associated with tobacco interests is unconscionable. How can Americans believe political promises for health care reform when both parties seem to be associated with an industry that disseminates disease, disability, and death."
—C. EVERETT KOOP, M.D.,
quoted in Tobacco Money, Tobacco People, Tobacco Policies, *published by Public Citizen and the Advocacy Institute, 1992*

Few people have had as great a struggle as Steve Hudner in

```
DAY  3 1 3
```

giving up smoking. When he smokes, there's no tomorrow, and he smokes like a chimney. And yet he says, "I feel terrible when I smoke. My teeth feel like they're falling out. My whole physiology changes. Every single cigarette I smoke tastes awful, even the one after dinner."

Hudner stopped for years and smoked again. Then he stopped for months and smoked again. Then he got onto a merry-go-round of weeks of smoking, weeks of not smoking. "When I pick up that first cigarette again, it always makes me sick. . . . And yet, there's nothing like it. You can have what you want. You wanted a cigarette and now you have it. You can't beat that."

Only the true smoke addict will understand how Hudner feels. "Childish? Of course it's childish! I felt infinitely better in those years when I didn't smoke. I hope I've smoked my last cigarette."

❖   ❖

"The brain or nerves . . . suffer most from tobacco. In one sense the brain is the man. Not only must this delicate and sensitive organ be in perfect health, but the steam of vitalizing blood which flows upon it must come pure and undefiled in order for its perfect action."
—HENRY GIBBONS, M.D., Tobacco and Its Effects, 1868

Because smoking is such a
powerful constrictor of blood
vessels, smokers are heavily represented among people with
too little blood getting to their lower limbs. Generally arteriosclerosis underlies the condition, and an ischemic (blood-poor)
foot is painful, cold, and often numb. The skin may be dry and
scaly, and ulceration may appear; a severely ischemic leg can
become shrunken and withered. If the blood is cut off between
the femoral and popliteal arteries in the leg, a bypass operation can save the leg before gangrene takes it away.

In 1989, the *Annals of Vascular Surgery* revealed the correlation between smoking and operative success on 103 smoking patients with lower limb ischemia, 43 of whom stopped
smoking after the operation. The 34 patients who continued to
smoke more than 15 cigarettes a day after the operation were
five times as likely to lose a limb within the next two years.

A 1960 Mayo Clinic study followed 159 patients with peripheral artery disease. Of the patients who continued to
smoke, 11 percent required amputations. Of those who did
not smoke, not one lost a limb.

❖ ❖

*The Odds: A 1991 study gave evidence that diabetics who
smoke have notably higher risks for early renal damage and
loss of sight.*

When "everybody" smoked, smoking wasn't seen as a disa-

bility, and not all smokers were heavily dependent on cigarettes. Some people just smoked for the fun of it. But now only one in four Americans still smokes, and most of these are serious addicts. (The American Psychiatric Association classified nicotine dependence as a psychiatric ailment in 1980.)

In these remaining hard-core smokers, there is probably some genetic basis for smoking, if only one of personality. Smokers may feel a much greater need than nonsmokers to adjust their neurotransmitters—something nicotine does. Smokers and ex-smokers are twice as prone to serious depression as nonsmokers. And some minority of smokers get seriously depressed when they stop smoking.

A predilection to smoke is not a reason to smoke. It is only a reason to understand why stopping is more difficult for some people and why further treatment may be in order. Depression is a treatable problem, and smoking isn't the answer. In many ways, some people have to work harder than others to be happy. Whatever "the genetic basis" for smoking might be, vast numbers of people have it, and right now more of them aren't smoking than are.

❖ ❖

"The older you get, the more you realize you're destined to be trapped by certain aspects of your personality. The best you can do is put a leash on them."
—WILLIAM A. O'LOUGHLIN, JR.,
ex-smoker, talk show host,
quoted in The New York Times, *October 4, 1992*

Women who both smoke and take birth control pills are at high risk for heart attacks and strokes—7 to 34 times more vulnerable than nonsmokers, according to one study. The risk rises with age, heading upward after age 30. Doctors are advised never to prescribe oral contraceptives to smokers over 35.

"I suggest diaphragms or condoms or sometimes tubal ligation for women over 35 who smoke," says Dr. Sadja Greenwood, a family practice physician. "Such women are poor risks for pregnancy anyhow. They have more fertility problems and miscarriages, low birth-weight babies, and more risks to the pregnancy in general.

"Unfortunately, an awful lot of women smoke out of fear of gaining weight, and it's one of the big reasons teenage girls start. It's normal to gain a little weight on quitting smoking for metabolic reasons, but you don't have to get fat. I tell people to start a walking program and keep lots of low-calorie reward foods around, like popcorn and carrot sticks, so they can go on putting something in their mouths all the time."

❖　❖

"Women have been clearly identified as a key target group for tobacco advertising in both the industrialized and developing worlds. Billions of U.S. dollars each year are spent on promoting this lethal product specifically to women."

—*Amanda Amos and Claire Chollat-Tarquet*,
World Health, 1990

People who call themselves en-
vironmentalists should not be

caught with cigarettes in their hands. Tobacco is a disastrous crop. No other plant robs the ground of more nutrients, and tobacco fields use tremendous amounts of both fertilizers and pesticides.

In many areas, fuel (such as wood, gas, or oil) is used for the curing of tobacco. In Kenya and Tanzania, tobacco curing uses 1 to 2 percent of all the wood burned. In Malawi, where large forests are being destroyed, a third of the wood supply goes to the curing of tobacco. The land on which tobacco grows could be far better used, particularly in many poor countries growing tobacco for export. If all the world's tobacco land were producing grain, it would feed 10 to 20 million people.

Cigarette factories, which use many chemicals, pollute the air and water. People who work in both tobacco fields and factories are the victims of many illnesses. And the environmentalist must consider that, when he smokes, he himself becomes a small factory spewing forth toxins into the air.

❖ ❖

Vox Populi: In 1698, the citizens of Saragossa, Spain, petitioned the town to stop the erection of a tobacco factory on the grounds that it would menace public health. The town council did so.

| D A Y   3 1 8 | Young smokers generally feel that they needn't worry about dread diseases until they reach more advanced ages. A study of the lungs of young males leaves doubt about this hopeful calculation.

The study compared 20 dead nonsmokers with 19 dead smokers. All were under 40, and half of them were under 25. Among the smokers, the mean cigarette consumption was 20 pack years. All of them had died suddenly outside the hospital, and relatives supplied their smoking histories. All their lungs were biopsied to determine changes in the peripheral airways.

Every one of the 19 smokers had inflammations in the bronchiole (small airway) tubes, as did only five of the nonsmokers—who had very mild cases or other reasons for respiratory difficulties. The lesions consisted of clusters of brown-pigmented macrophages (large white blood cells). These are lesions that seem to play a role in the later development of emphysema.

At this early stage, little noteworthy tissue destruction had taken place, and so it is probable that the damage was still reversible. The smokers also demonstrated several other abnormalities, but ones of less significance than the respiratory bronchiolitis.

❖   ❖

"Nobody on the team smokes. No one at all. It's an endurance thing."

—JOHN TAYLOR, *NFL wide receiver, San Francisco '49ers*

Most cigarette fires could be prevented if cigarettes didn't

go on burning when no one is puffing. In a typical cigarette fire, someone carelessly or sleepily drops a burning cigarette. It is likely to take ten or fifteen minutes before the couch or the bed—or the forest—lights up.

So why not market cigarettes that don't go on burning by themselves? Untreated tobacco—as in pipes and cigars—is self-extinguishing. Only the tobacco companies know what makes cigarettes keep burning, and they won't tell, but it seems to be either added nitrates, nitrates from fertilizers, or something added to the papers. There is great variation in the burning times of different cigarettes, and it would be no great trick to make cigarettes that extinguish themselves—it's been done.

However, the tobacco companies will have none of it. The customers don't want to relight their cigarettes, they say. Which may be true, but few smokers would have to relight a cigarette that burned for a couple of minutes on its own. Stingy customers might even appreciate a cigarette that didn't burn away by itself. Then they wouldn't have to go out and buy new cigarettes so often—but the tobacco companies might not like that.

❖ ❖

TOBACCO POWER: *Years ago, Representative John Moss of California tried to pass a bit of legislation that would regulate cigarettes as fire ignition sources. Said Tom Greene, a member of Moss's staff: "I thought we'd probably do okay on this, it seemed like such a motherhood issue. We just got blown out of the water. Those guys [the tobacco lobby] are tough."*

"A national program to meet the tobacco epidemic has to have three essential components," says Garfield Mahood of the Nonsmokers' Rights Association of Canada. These are:

1. Preventing children from joining the market. Laws against selling to children must be enforced, and the best way to accomplish this is through the licensing of retailers. Where cigarettes are sold, they should be under-the-counter items.
2. Establishing informed consent between buyer and seller. This means eliminating all advertising, which is entirely deceptive, and establishing an effective warning system about the dangers of tobacco industry products.
3. Protecting people from environmental tobacco smoke (ETS). "In the workplace," says Mahood, "there are two acceptable solutions. One is to ban smoking altogether and the other is to confine smoking to separate vented lounges, which are exhausted to the outdoors. What is not a solution is to leave it to workers individually to demand nonsmoking workplaces. For many workers, that's a nonright, because the nonsmoker who raises a fuss at work suffers. ETS should be treated as any other toxin. You don't leave controls on benzene or vinyl chloride up to the workers."

Fact: An EPA study found that, largely due to smoking, indoor levels of toxic pollutants are up to 20 times higher than outdoor levels.

Steve Crisman had a heart attack the day after his engage-

ment to Mariel Hemingway. The 35-year-old New York
restaurateur was a longtime smoker of unfiltered Camels and
until that moment didn't think he could ever stop. His only am-
bition was to cut down.

On the day of the heart attack, he and Hemingway were
vacationing in a remote cabin in Montana. Crisman was air-
lifted to the nearest hospital. Hemingway, not allowed to ride
in the helicopter, was left behind. She knew why 35-year-old
men have heart attacks and so, while she waited and worried,
she burned Crisman's cigarettes.

Happily, Crisman recuperated. What's more, he never
smoked again. Fear took his taste for cigarettes away. Today,
he is an enthusiastic nonsmoker and a lover of fresh air.

❖ ❖

*"Whenever I see young people smoking I can't help myself
from saying, 'How in the world can you smoke? You grew
up in a society where you knew it was a killer. . . . Don't
start a habit that can only hurt.'"*

—MARIEL HEMINGWAY

Certain products—such as computer chips—have to be manufactured in a room entirely free of dust and other contaminants. Companies making these items install elaborate air-filtering systems and workers wear special suits with face masks and gloves.

With all precautions taken, companies discovered one final problem: Smokers exhale particulate matter for as long as an hour after their last cigarette. Stuart Hoenig at the University of Arizona found that a smoker exhales 30,000 particles one minute after smoking a cigarette to a nonsmoker's 1,000 particles.

Most of the particles were analyzed as surface cells from the mouth. Ten minutes after smoking, the smoker was down to about 6,000 particles. The best solution proved to be for smokers to drink water before returning to the clean room. Most of the particles washed down.

❖ ❖

SIGN SIGHTED IN ARTIST'S STUDIO:

THANK YOU FOR NOT SMOKING

Cigarette smoke is the residue of your pleasure. It contaminates the air and pollutes my hair and clothes, not to mention my lungs.

THIS TAKES PLACE WITHOUT MY CONSENT

I have a pleasure also; I like a beer now and again. The residue from my pleasure is urine. Would you be annoyed if I stood on a chair and pissed on your head and clothes without your consent?

Cancer of the penis need not be the biggest worry of a

smoking man, particularly if he is circumcised, but it should register. A study in Sweden found men who smoked more than ten cigarettes a day with over twice the risk of nonsmokers for penile cancer.

Penile cancer is rare among circumcised men and most common in men with phimosis—a condition in which the foreskin cannot be withdrawn over the head of the penis—but smoking was found in the Swedish study to be independent of phimosis. It is possible that tobacco products become concentrated in smegma, making it carcinogenic.

❖ ❖

"Thus do I take revenge in full upon the Spaniards for all their cruelty to the Indians; since by acquainting their conquerors with the use of tobacco I have done them greater injury than even the King of Spain through his agents ever did his victims; for it is both more honorable and more natural to die by a pike thrust or a cannon ball than from the ignoble effects of poisonous tobacco."

—A TOBACCO FIEND,
          speaking in an eighteenth-century epic

If you ever go back to smoking, your excuse will probably be that you were "under a lot of stress." But, if you are like most of the relapsers studied by psychologists Robert Gunn and Allison Shapiro, you will not actually be under any more stress than your counterpart who didn't smoke. Chances are good that some time later you won't even be able to remember what the trauma was that supposedly drove you back to smoking. In fact, Gunn and Shapiro discovered that the relapsers they interviewed had even fewer significant life changes than the people who didn't smoke.

It may be that the stress explanation is retroactive, produced to counter the guilt people feel at smoking. After all, most of us on any given day could make a case for feeling stress. So stress is no excuse, whether it's real or not. Giving up smoking should be like getting married: "For richer, for poorer, in sickness and in health, until death do us part."

❖ ❖

"Changing just four factors in your life-style—giving up smoking; giving up alcohol; eating a high-fiber, low-fat vegetarian diet; and keeping normal weight—could prevent 75 percent of cancers found in Western society."
—AILEEN LUDINGTON, M.D.

Before his death of emphysema, Rear Admiral Gerald

Synhorst reflected on military smoking: "Just about everyone who mattered in my world smoked. . . . Uncle Sam made sure even the servicemen smoked. Cigarettes for the military during World War II, when they weren't free, were three cents a pack, seven cents a pack.

"We just gradually smoked more as pressures mounted. In dangerous waters 30 fathoms deep, where rival Russian subs could be lurking, pressures mounted often. We smoked. When carbon monoxide levels became too high in the submarines, everyone might have to quit smoking temporarily, but when the air cleared we lit up again.

"We were happy. Innocent of our time bomb. But the enemy was not the Russian surveillance sub watching us—the enemy was the deadly little white-and-brown weapon in our own hands. But we didn't know we were watching our good men commit suicide slowly—forsaking their posts. If we were forfeiting our country's proud warriors to the enemy, we didn't know it.

" 'Marlboro' means impotency and death for country men . . . not clean, fresh air in the lungs."

❖ ❖

"I hope I will have enough strength to warn all the young navy and army men and women and young people everywhere . . . 'Take time out to fight your addictions before they fell you!' "

—REAR ADMIRAL GERALD SYNHORST,
The Saturday Evening Post, 1986

"My grandfather always broke or ruined something when he came to visit," says one nonsmoker. "My mother's prize white marble coffee table got a permanent bright orange stain when he left a cigarette burning on the edge. For years afterwards, I always thought of him when I saw that stain."

Smokers have improved their manners since then, but being a smoker is still a bit like going around with a bad dog on a leash. You have to be exceptional for anyone to want you at all. Apartment owners don't want you. Being left with the stink of tobacco in carpets and drapes is an unwelcome proposition. Employers don't want you. You cost them too much. Hostesses don't want you. You'll puff and dirty up their houses.

Smokers themselves often don't much care for the places left for them—the smelly smoking cars on trains, the small rooms, gray with smoke, assigned to smokers in office buildings. In bars a smoker can light up with little censure, but it's a restrained spouse who has no comment on the smell when the bar habitué returns home.

❖ ❖

"When I gave up smoking, I adopted another companion to keep me company when I was alone. I became a friend to myself."

—ERNEST CALDWELL, Stop Smoking, 1959

One of the most underrated losses smokers suffer is the

sense of smell. Smokers are rarely aware of what they're missing. They can still smell the coffee in the morning. The can sort of taste their food. And loss of smell doesn't seem terribly important next to not being able to breathe, walk, and so on.

But smell goes far beyond fresh-baked bread and lilacs in spring. No other sense inspires the immediacy of feeling that smell does, and the nose is the touchstone to the richest memories.

❖ ❖

"This lovely smell [an old quilt] is one of a broad group of delicate smells that were lost to me for 24 years because I was addicted to cigarettes. The sense of smell is not an intellectual sense such as sight and hearing. . . . so a smart guy like me thinks he can give up smell for the pleasure of smoking. A few days after I stopped, I began to notice the vast realm of smells that were lost all those years. I began breathing in a life I hadn't felt since I was 17, like seeing grass after a quarter-century at the South Pole.

"I smelled creamed peas and onions, wood smells, dirt smells. Walked into an old garage, and a hundred smells jumped out, the spirits of a hundred old men in undershirts mixing shellac and sanding a screen door and oiling a rifle and patching an innertube. A hidden life came back to me, the ordinary days of long ago when I sat with the others and talked on the porch and had a little chow."

—GARRISON KEILLOR, **Leaving Home,** *1987*

Many companies are still struggling with the problem of what to do about smokers. The ones that aren't are those that have simply banned smoking altogether. Those that have tried to settle for a mixed-bag policy continue to have troubles.

In 1983, Pacific Northwest Bell (PNB) outlawed smoking in meeting rooms and let individual work groups decide how to designate their areas. Much discontent ensued. Complaints about drifting smoke could have been resolved only with prohibitively expensive ventilation systems. So in 1985, PNB's president announced to the company's 15,000 workers: "To protect the health and safety of PNB employees, there will be no smoking in any company facility."

There was little negative reaction. Companies often worry that employees will waste excessive time smoking outdoors, but the PNB human resources director thinks that instead productivity increased; fewer employees now smoke. Even smokers often appreciate the incentive to decrease or end their smoking.

The alternate policy of setting up designated smoking areas becomes an expensive benefit for a minority of the employees. Texas Instruments spent $500,000 trying to retrofit its buildings and still had a problem with smoke drifting back into no-smoking areas.

❖   ❖

"I often have lunch in the Philip Morris cafeteria, and there are so few people in the smoking section that it's almost embarrassing."

—ANONYMOUS ATTORNEY

Cecil Asman quit smoking on November 16, 1971, after

DAY 329

twenty-plus years of smoking and three years of trying to quit. "By the time I decided to quit I was up to two to three packs a day, and I can honestly say that of all those cigarettes I only enjoyed the one after breakfast and the one after dinner. I stopped the first time six weeks before President Kennedy was shot, and by the time the weekend of his funeral was over, I was smoking again just as before.

"I tried chewing toothpicks, eating carrot sticks, and puffing on cigarettes with holes in them. And still I smoked. Then one day I went to a seminar at the Holiday Inn, which was some kind of personal evaluation thing, nothing to do with smoking. As I walked out the door, a voice said—my own voice—'You've just stopped smoking.' This may sound corny, but it was almost a religious experience. I haven't had a cigarette since.

"Strangely enough, I didn't have the withdrawal symptoms I'd had before. It was all over at once. I just felt 'Oh, my God, I've done it!' I'd had a horrible hacking cough and that went away quickly. I used to wonder how I could go on smoking when it made me feel so badly."

❖   ❖

"Even though I quit smoking in 1969, sometimes I still dream that I'm smoking and that I'm sick and feel horrible. After I wake up, it takes a moment before the relief that it was just a dream comes over me."

—LARRY C. WHITE, *ex-smoker*

| D A Y   3 3 0 | Smoking is becoming more and more a low-income sport.

It is generally assumed that poor people smoke more because they're oppressed, uneducated, have boring jobs, and don't plan for the future. What should be considered is that perhaps they're poor because they smoke.

Take Family A: They live in New York City. Mom smokes, let's say a pack and a half a day. She buys by the carton and so spends about $1,200 a year on her habit.

Take Family B: Nobody smokes. They invest $1,200 a year at compound interest. In twenty years, they're sitting on $59,000. Maybe not quite enough for four years at Yale, but plenty to send a kid through the State University.

Take Family C: Mom and Dad both smoke, between them three and a half packs a day. This adds up to $3,000 a year (which could be $148,000 in twenty years). Having never gotten together the down payment on a house, they are facing old age with little security.

The price of cigarettes is actually the smaller part of smokers' costs, which include time out for sickness, extra medical care, higher insurance, holes in the furniture and clothes, and so on. Family C's kids are a lot more likely to grow up and smoke than Family B's, thus impeding another generation's rise up the economic ladder. Whether or not smoking makes people poor, it certainly contributes to keeping them that way.

❖   ❖

"I never saw a well man in the exercise of common sense who could say that tobacco did him any good."
—WILL H. BROWN,
Tobacco Under the Searchlight, 1925

Why is it that a mother's smoking seems to have so many

bad effects on babies? Because tobacco directly affects the fetus, crossing the placenta and shortchanging the baby on oxygen and nutrients.

While the smoking mother has increased levels of carbon monoxide, the amount is twice as high in the baby—carbon monoxide passes rapidly across the placenta—thus reducing the oxygen supply. Then, because nicotine narrows blood vessels, the baby receives fewer nutrients. It may be that nicotine also directly injures the developing brain, where nicotine concentrates. The baby's adrenal and pituitary glands also absorb high doses. If the mother smokes only two cigarettes, a baby's chest movements slow down.

Nicotine and carbon dioxide aren't the only worries. Tobacco smoke is made up of some 4,000 chemicals, and a great many of them could be having some unknown and unfortunate effect. No prospective mother should smoke, nor should she and her baby be passive smokers. If other family members smoke, they should step outdoors to do it.

We might note that not every problem has been blamed on smoking. No evidence has arisen that smoking is associated with mental retardation, cerebral palsy, or seizures.

❖ ❖

FACT: Hemoglobin levels in newborns reflect the number of cigarettes mothers smoked during pregnancy.

A fifth of the people living in the developed world today will die of smoking-related diseases. While millions of these deaths will be from cancer, an even greater number will be from heart disease and stroke.

More than half of these deaths will be of middle-aged people (35 to 69), who will average a loss of life of 23 years each. Consistently throughout middle age, the death rates of cigarette smokers are more than twice the rates of nonsmokers. In Poland, fully half the deaths of middle-aged men will be from smoking diseases.

The highest European death rates are in Great Britain and Germany. The deaths of women from smoking are rising throughout the developed world and will continue to rise for some years to come, even while smoking rates are dropping. In the U.S.A., 37 percent of women who die between the ages of 35 and 69 will die from tobacco use.

❖   ❖

"Mr. Pickett [the ambulance driver] reaches the caller's home to find an ashen-faced man slumped beside a butt-choked ashtray. The stricken man quit smoking three years ago, following a coronary, but started again after a few weeks. 'He was feeling OK by then,' his wife explains."

—**The Wall Street Journal,** *September 22, 1992, an article on life in Glasgow, Scotland, where 83 percent of middle-aged men smoked at one time and coronary death rates are 800 percent higher than in Japan.*

In 1954, when the news was just breaking that tobacco was carcinogenic, the tobacco companies banded together and set up a "research" arm—the Council for Tobacco Research (CTR). The actual intent of CTR was to cast doubt on all evidence that cigarettes caused disease. *The Wall Street Journal* opened a recent article on CTR by saying, "This is the story of the longest-running misinformation campaign in history . . ."

CTR scoured the world for pro-tobacco studies to fund, for cancer-resistant strains of mice, for hungry scientists willing to put up with its interference. Unfavorable results of CTR research were distorted or covered up. CTR made controversy where otherwise none existed and continued to assert that the connection between lung cancer and smoking has not been proven.

It is possible, however, that the ploys of CTR will prove the undoing of the tobacco industry. The Supreme Court ruled in 1992 that smokers can file suits on the grounds that the tobacco industry knowingly deceived them. So far, the tobacco industry has never been held liable for a sick smoker, but should the tide turn, tobacco companies could go down like the asbestos companies of yore.

❖   ❖

". . . they kept providing false reassurances, so I had no idea that smoking was so very dangerous."
—JANET SACKMAN [*former Miss Lucky Strike, now ill with throat cancer*],
The Wall Street Journal, *February 11, 1993*

You've added up eleven months without smoking now, and it's none too soon to start planning a celebration for your first anniversary. It's a great occasion for a party. One of the things you're celebrating is your ability to enjoy yourself without smoking. You may have some new faces on your guest list, too—people who got friendlier after you stopped smoking.

You may have gotten friendlier yourself since you gave up your cigarettes. On losing the solace of tobacco, people often deepen their relationships with others. While, unlike cigarettes, your friends may sometimes have engagements elsewhere, they are infinitely more various and interesting.

At your anniversary party, a nice ceremonial would be to have each person talk about his or her experiences in giving up smoking or in being a nonsmoker in a world which was until recently too civil to smokers. Perhaps your guests could consider what further contribution you could make to a smokefree year 2000—beyond the all-important one of your present examples.

❖ ❖

"In the chronicle of human pleasure cigarette smoking is a gruesomely freakish phenomenon. In any universal sense cigarettes have existed for scarcely a couple of generations, and their toxicity and carcinogenic nature have been scientifically validated only in the past 25 years. They should be regarded, then, as the vile little marauders that they are, possessing no merit and vast lethal capacity, needing to be banished with the passion that we banish any other product that we innocently adopt only to discover that it endangers our lives."
—WILLIAM STYRON, The Nation, *March 7, 1987*

A feeling of emptiness may be at the root of more smoking

than anything else. Something's missing. You don't know what. You smoke. And something's there! The problem is that it's all smoke, inside and out. It's not love or respect or peace or beauty. It doesn't give you a sense of involvement or fulfillment or wisdom. It doesn't even get dinner on the table. Smoking just wastes time and money and makes you sick.

So you quit, and you feel empty. And seeing you've got that hole there, you're likely to look around for ways to fill it. You've had eleven months now of trying to fill the hole up in other ways.

You're probably more active. Very likely you're more involved in some aspect or other of life. Your relationships may be deeper. It may not even seem all to the good. Perhaps you've started a feud with your neighbors, adding an unpleasant kind of zip to your life. Try something else.

You may very likely still feel a hole. Eleven months isn't very long for filling up holes so keep looking and be conscious of what helps. If something you do helps fill the hole, whether it's volunteer work or going to the opera or folk dancing, do it again.

❖   ❖

"Happiness or enjoyment is a product of meaningful activity."
—RICHARD REKOW, *theater director*

| D A Y   3 3 6 | Children of smokers don't just suffer from bronchitis, asthma, and pneumonia. They also have increases in the more pedestrian complaints: wheezing, coughing, and allergies.

A slew of studies have shown increased wheezing and coughing in children in smoking families. In South Korea, a study of 3,651 children found a dose-response relationship for chronic coughing, which was 2.4 times more likely in children whose family members smoked 1 to 14 cigarettes a day and 3.2 times more likely in children when family members smoked more than 15 cigarettes daily. In another study of 5,953 infants, mothers who smoked more than 3 cigarettes a day reported 2.7 times as much wheezing in their children.

A Japanese study followed 48 wheezy infants. Four years later, 17 of the 18 children who were still wheezy were smokers' children. Numerous studies also show children of smokers suffering disproportionately from coughing and phlegm. Most of the evidence relates to young children, but one study showed more coughing among high school athletes who came from smoking homes. Children of smokers are also significantly more likely to have allergies than children of nonsmokers.

SAD FACT: The children of smokers have been shown to have diminished lung function, a condition that may follow them into adulthood. They are also only half as likely to be in good health as the children of nonsmokers.

Old smokers may like to think that smoking can't damage

them much more. Some studies have given a bit of substance to this fantasy. Statistically, one would certainly expect a less powerful effect from smoking when the whole age group is dying fast of many other things. Raymond Pearl, who in 1938 did a pathbreaking longevity study of smokers, wrote: "Those individuals in the damaged groups who survive to 70 or thereabouts are such tough and resistant specimens that thereafter tobacco does them no further measurable harm as a group."

Perhaps you don't have to be so unusually resilient to get to 70 anymore. These days, old smokers still lose years from their life expectancies from continued smoking. A 1987 study showed smokers aged 70 or over dying at 1.43 times the rate of nonsmokers. The Honolulu Heart Program followed 1,394 men between the ages of 65 and 74. Over a twelve-year period, the smokers had 1.62 times the number of heart problems as the nonsmokers. The ex-smokers fell halfway between the nonsmokers and the currents, showing that the beneficial effect of quitting holds true even in later life.

❖ ❖

"Now that I'm gone, I tell you: Don't smoke, whatever you do, just don't smoke."
        —YUL BRYNNER (1920–1985), in TV commercial, 1986

| D A Y   3 3 8 | Adults as well as children get
respiratory problems from sec-
ondhand smoke. Because of all the other stuff people are exposed to, it is difficult to document the effect of secondhand
smoke on the lungs, but six substantial studies released since
1987 have shown degrees of damage.

In tests of 1,245 American never-smoking men, those married to smokers exhaled more carbon dioxide and had lower
scores on lung function tests. A study of hospitalized Greek
women found that those with pulmonary problems were 1.9
times more likely to have smoking husbands. A third study of
thousands of nonsmoking American and French women discovered more wheezing, coughing, and shortness of breath in the
ones married to smokers.

The results were subtle enough to suggest that there are
probably people who are bothered very little by secondhand
smoke (perhaps due to drafty houses). These people, however,
are balanced by the estimated 3,000 individuals who annually get lung cancer from secondhand smoke and the thousands of other nonsmokers who die from Chronic Obstructive
Pulmonary Disease (COPD). Were these deaths caused by any
other carcinogen, that substance would be banned.

❖ ❖

*"Employers should be especially aware of the health risks
associated with passive smoking. I doubt that wives will
sue their husbands for damages caused by exposure to
secondhand smoke in the home, but employees probably
will sue their employers for damages caused by similar
exposure in the workplace."*
—MARTIN J. MARTIN, M.D., *clinical epidemiologist*

Americans have been known to return home from travels in France complaining bitterly that the air everywhere is foul with tobacco smoke. Although, in fact, the French smoke fewer cigarettes per capita than Americans, a higher percentage are smokers, and they often do their smoking in the same cafés and bars tourists patronize.

But if France seemed like a smoker's paradise once, it isn't anymore. On November 1, 1993, a new law banned tobacco advertising, sales to minors, and smoking in all public places, including restaurants. In a culture in which smoking between courses was routine, this seems extraordinary. But France has been paying a high price for smoking. Approximately 61,000 of its citizens die yearly from the habit, their sicknesses paid for by the state. Cigarettes are a revenue-producing government monopoly, but not one that pays off in the long run.

According to the early reports, the new law banning smoking in public places has not been widely observed. Travelers should not get their hopes too high.

❖ ❖

TOBACCO ECONOMICS: *Noting that the government paid out three francs in health costs for every one franc collected in tobacco sales, an unusually outspoken French finance minister of some years back remarked, "But I get the one franc. It is my successor who will have to pay out the three francs."*

Judy Morris spent years trying to quit smoking and finally turned the corner on her fortieth birthday. By this time, she was willing to give up coffee, alcohol, and parties where people were smoking. "Whatever you have to do to stop is worth it," says Morris. "Turning forty, I knew I wasn't feeling as well as I should. Now I've got more energy, I can smell, my skin looks better, and my kids are glad.

"The psychological part takes a lot longer to deal with than the physical. I was nervous and teary at first, and I had to learn how to deal with stress by doing something besides reaching for a cigarette. It's important for people to know that the urge to smoke doesn't disappear in a few months. The first few times I quit I let down my guard too soon. It took me a couple of years to really get over cigarettes."

❖   ❖

"I have discovered that I labored under about a 25 percent handicap while I was smoking; now, having quit smoking and dealing with the same theoretical and practical problems, I realize that I am able to comprehend, reason and calculate much more clearly and rapidly. I regret the years spent working at lowered capacity."

—PRIZE-WINNING MIT SCIENTIST, *ex-smoker,*
quoted in You Can Stop *by Jacquelyn Rogers, 1977*

The tobacco industry has been

fairly successful at obstructing antismoking legislation at the federal and state levels. But it has been losing at the local level. Now it is fighting town by town, county by county.

How, one wonders, can tobacco lobbyists affect particular legislation in hundreds of communities across the country? Big money and big computers are the keys. In the computers are the names of millions of smokers. When antismoking legislation pops up in a community, a tobacco representative arrives to mold the local smokers into an impressive "grassroots" movement fighting for their "rights." Aided by law firms, public relations agencies, and manpower furnished by the tobacco industry, the smokers' rights group can make an impact.

Victory is not assured, however. If the local health community is organized and local politicians are committed, the rights of nonsmokers are upheld. Willing as the tobacco industry may be to fight on the beaches, in the fields, and in the streets, the tide has turned.

❖ ❖

"We must somehow do a better job than we have in the past in getting our side of the story told to city councils and county commissions. Over time, we can lose the battle over smoking restrictions as decisively in bits and pieces—at the local level—as with state or federal measures."
        —RAYMOND PRITCHARD,
            chairman of Brown and Williamson Tobacco

An individual's cancer risk rises with each additional household member who smokes. Those who have been exposed to tobacco in both childhood and adulthood are the most threatened. Many diseases, such as asthma and emphysema, can be caused entirely by passive smoking, the risk increasing with the amount of exposure. Chronic workplace exposure adds again another significant burden.

❖ ❖

"Both the smoker and the nonsmoker are breathing the same 4,000 or so constituents of cigarette smoke. They're both inhaling the same tars, the same naphthalene and the same pyrene and benaopyrene. They absorb the same carbon monoxide, methane, ammonia, acetylene and hydrogen cyanide. . . . This ought to be alarming news for the two-thirds of the American adult population—the people who do not now smoke—or, let's say, the people who think they do not now smoke."

—C. EVERETT KOOP, *former surgeon general*

"I finally managed to stop smoking when I was pregnant

with my second child," says Kathy Fields. "I figured it was my last chance to quit as I'd never have a better incentive. I was devoted to smoking. I remember lighting up at a party many years ago and having the hostess primly announce, 'Oh, I don't allow smoking in *my* home.' Without thinking, I snapped, 'Well! If I'd known *that*, I wouldn't have come.'

"I quit cold turkey but did things to reward myself each day, like putting the money I would have spent on cigarettes in a special jar. The first couple of weeks were hell. It was at least six weeks before the benefits were apparent, but then I noticed that my breath was back, and my mouth tasted clean in the morning, and it was great not to have to buy, carry, and worry about running out of cigarettes. I felt free.

"I wasn't completely liberated, though, because for three or four years I went on bumming cigarettes at parties or buying a pack once in a while and smoking a couple. Finally several years ago, I smoked my last one. It's much better not to have even any attachment. I hate it now when people smoke around me, but I'm in sympathy with them. How can they stand to fly? I remember very well that cellular pain of needing a cigarette and not having one."

❖   ❖

"I always had a lot of energy, but since quitting I've got more time so I get a lot done. Smoking was another excuse for procrastinating."

—KATHY FIELDS, *ex-smoker*

Female smokers may find themselves passing anemia tests that they should be flunking. A feature of smoking is that it raises the hemoglobin reading, and consequently anemia in smokers is underestimated. Almost twice as many nonsmokers as smokers test as anemic.

An article in *The Journal of American Medicine* recommends that smokers be screened by a slightly different scale than nonsmokers. Whereas the accepted cutoff for women is now 120 g/L, the article suggests that for smokers of 10 to 19 cigarettes a day, the cutoff should be 123 g/L; for smokers of 20–39 cigarettes, it should be 125 g/L; and for those smoking more than 40 cigarettes a day, it should be 127 g/L.

The exaggerated reading is related to smokers' high exposure to carbon monoxide, which bonds to hemoglobin to form carboxyhemoglobin, an inactive form of hemoglobin that has no oxygen-carrying capacity. Smokers with high levels of carboxyhemoglobin fatigue easily and have a shortage of blood reaching the heart during exercise.

On quitting smoking, the recovery is rapid, and ex-smokers have normal levels of hemoglobin.

❖ ❖

Fact: Numerous drugs are less effective—or even ineffective—when taken by smokers.

Barbara Czerny smoked for 45 years and stopped when

she was diagnosed with Chronic Obstructive Pulmonary Disease (COPD). Because she was so sick, she hardly noticed the withdrawal. But much later, she discovered how much smoking had meant to her.

"Six months after I quit I found myself crying at supermarket openings, and then I knew how much I missed my cigarettes. Cigarettes are a very good friend. They're there when you're sad, they're there when you're bored, they're there when you're nervous. Then when you no longer have cigarettes, and life starts handing you problems, you don't know how to deal with them. The crying continued for about two months and then it just went away.

"I used to think I couldn't function without cigarettes, but now smoking has no appeal for me at all. In fact, it's very bad if I smell smoke because my lungs just close down. Because of smoking, I'm on prednisone, a drug that killed one friend of mine and is now killing another. But with my condition, the choice is to either not breathe or to take it. People should do whatever they have to do to quit smoking."

❖   ❖

"The respiratory system has well-developed protective mechanisms, particularly in the conducting airways through which the air reaches the deep lungs; however, the ultimate surfaces of exposure, the alveolar membranes, are extremely delicate and fragile and highly vulnerable to toxic agents which reach them."
—Environmental Factors in Respiratory Diseases, *edited by Douglas H. K. Lee, 1973*

Denial is the linchpin of the defiant smoker's practice. A cough is a sinus problem, puffing on the stairs is normal, he couldn't possibly feel better, and he simply hasn't got time for regular exercise. These small dishonesties are aggravating to nonsmokers, who are expected to swallow this nonsense, rather than to retort with, "Who are you kidding?"

In the case of smokers with family members dying of smoking diseases, the denial often becomes monumental. Most victims of lung cancer not only smoke but come from families of smokers. Like many diseases, lung cancer strikes some families more than others.

The Johns Hopkins Oncology Center conducted a study of the relatives of patients newly diagnosed with lung cancer. Six months after the diagnosis, only 8 percent of the relatives had quit smoking. Only 22 percent were even willing to go to a cessation program. While 82 percent of them were aware that smoking causes lung cancer, only 36 percent thought that smoking was responsible for the lung cancer of the stricken family member, and only 8 percent perceived that having a family member with cancer might indicate a vulnerability to cancer in themselves.

❖ ❖

HINC ILLAE LACRIMAE (THUS THESE TEARS): *Joseph Lerner, the founder of the Lerner Shops, had over forty operations for aerodigestive cancers, eventually losing his tongue, jawbone, larynx, and upper esophagus. He both breathed and ate through tubes, and the cancers at last killed him. His son, Alan Jay Lerner, the composer of* My Fair Lady, *was also a smoker and died of lung cancer.*

Two groups scheduled for surgery, one smoking and one

nonsmoking, were studied in regard to their need for oxygen immediately following the operations. The smokers required considerably more oxygen, despite the fact that as a group they were younger than the nonsmokers. As it is desirable for patients to return to normal breathing as soon as possible after surgery, this is one more of many signs that the smoking surgery patient has a lot to be nervous about.

❖ ❖

"And when the Pipe grows foul within,
Think on thy soul defiled with sin,
And then the fire it doth require
Thus think, then drinke Tobacco.

The ashes that are left behind,
May serve to put thee still in mind,
That unto dust, return thou must
Thus think, then drink Tobacco."

—THOMAS JENNER, **The Soul's Solace**, 1626

| D A Y   3 4 8 | Anyone who was a flight attendant before the domestic smoking ban knows the unpleasantness of working in a flying can of smoke. For many of them, the constant exposure led to ongoing health problems. For a few, cancer and death were the sequels.

Nonsmoking flight attendants have now filed a $5 billion class action suit in Dade County, Florida, against the tobacco companies. The suit claims that the tobacco companies knowingly distributed a poisonous product that injured the plaintiffs prior to the federal airline smoking ban. This is the first lawsuit brought by nonsmokers against the tobacco industry.

Flight attendants and passengers on international flights continue to be smoke victims, as do air passengers in many of the countries of the world. Many flyers have exclaimed at how much more tolerable flying in the U.S. has become since the smoke ban. The thought of a long international flight is enough to keep some of us at home.

❖ ❖

"I would be infinitely more comfortable representing John Gotti than the president of Philip Morris. Lawyers tend to talk about smoking in abstract terms like 'liberty' and 'rights,' but all this is nonsense regarding tobacco. Tobacco has no redeeming qualities. It is a killer; it is the most evil product on the face of the earth."

—STANLEY ROSENBLATT,
*attorney representing flight attendants
in class action suit against tobacco companies*

Given the state of public information regarding smoking,

why isn't everyone who still smokes desperately trying to stop? Why, instead of going to Rome for holidays, don't they choose stop-smoking cruises or backpacking trips away from cigarettes? Smokers with bad knees take time off from work for surgery but don't take time off to deal with their greater disability—smoking.

"It's got to be a mental problem," says one aging widow who still smokes. "If you know something is very bad for you and will probably cut your life short and you don't do anything about it, then you can't add two and two. You're beyond the power of reason."

Such people often are operating under the illusion that smoking is making a useful contribution by reducing stress or alleviating depression. Tell them it isn't true.

❖ ❖

"Cancer specialists in general find that nine out of ten patients will stop smoking immediately upon hearing that they have a cancer caused by smoking. They will also confess that if, two weeks before the diagnosis, someone had told them they should stop, they would have found it impossible to do so. The remaining 10 percent are so shackled by nicotine that they will continue to smoke, even after surgery . . ."
—WILLIAM G. CAHAN, M.D.,
    Introduction to Smoking: The Artificial Passion, 1990

D A Y   3 5 0 COPD (Chronic Obstructive Pulmonary Disease) is the correct term for chronic bronchitis and emphysema in the advanced stages. COPD kills 60,000 people a year and is a contributing cause of death for more than twice that many. Because of the extra burden on the heart, people with emphysema are likely to die of heart failure.

Anyone who has smoked a pack a day for a number of years has the beginnings of emphysema. In emphysema, the air sacs of the lungs are breaking down, and the lungs are losing their ability to expel their contents. Instead of a proper air exchange, you've got old air stuck in your lungs. As the condition worsens, the ruptured air sacs combine into large balloonlike sacs, which look like clusters of grapes, and breathing becomes more and more difficult. Like Humpty Dumpty, ruptured air sacs can never be put back together again, but the person who quits smoking may stop the progress of the disease.

A chronic cough in a smoker should be taken seriously. Something is amiss. The cilia, which function in most people to bring up secretions, aren't functioning well, and the lungs are irritated. The cough could be an early symptom of COPD. People who quit smoking after being diagnosed with COPD are likely to extend their lives.

❖   ❖

EARLY GRAVE: Yuri Andropov died of emphysema in early 1984, just 14 months after succeeding Leonid Brezhnev as general secretary of the Soviet Union. He was 68 years old.

A pathbreaking recent study found more precancerous ab-

normalities in the lungs of women married to smokers than in the lungs of women married to nonsmokers. The lungs were provided by nonsmoking women who died in accidents in Attica, Greece.

This research, released by Harvard University in late 1992, was the first to visually demonstrate the medical connection between passive smoking and disease. Many studies have shown a statistical connection (wives of smokers more likely to get lung cancer), but such visible evidence as in this study makes the case against passive smoking far more convincing.

"The dramatic impact of passive smoke on these women can be compared to approximately 10 percent of the effect on the lungs suffered by active smokers," said Dr. Dimitrios Trichopoulos, who headed the Harvard team. Most of us ordinary citizens are already sold on the dangers of passive smoking, but the tobacco industry has steadfastly argued that statistical evidence was faulty. This latest evidence is harder to refute.

❖ ❖

THE CASUALTY LIST: *Secondhand smoke is currently estimated to cause not only 3,000 cases a year of lung cancer but also to contribute to the deaths of 40,000 Americans annually through heart disease.*

| D A Y   3 5 2 | Now that you've been smoke free for almost a year, you may feel an impulse to encourage someone else to quit. This is a fine impulse, but one is often uncertain as to how to go about doing it. Personal experience tells us that a smoker who feels picked on does not respond positively.

What you might do is make a little speech such as this: "It's been a year now since I stopped smoking, and I'm very happy I did. I once didn't think I could survive without cigarettes, but the rewards far outweigh the pain, and I feel better in every way. I want you to know that if you decide to quit, I'll help you in any way I can."

Should anyone take you up on your offer, make every effort to help. Drop by to visit on Day 1, telephone regularly, be sympathetic. Bring flowers, carrot sticks, or popcorn. Arrange no-smoking activities you can do together, such as walking, bicycling, and going to movies. Provide reassurance that the suffering will pass and that the future is bright.

If you would like to help others in a more organized way, call a local chapter of the American Lung Association, which uses volunteers in education, in policy work, and as facilitators in the Freedom From Smoking program. Numerous other organizations are also fighting for smoke-free air. With all hands on deck, a nonsmoking world is possible.

❖ ❖

"I have never felt or looked better and I attribute it to no more cigarettes. I encourage all of my friends to stop."
—SALLY KIRKLAND, *actress, ex-smoker*

With money from the state cig-

arette tax, the California De-
partment of Health Services financed a major report on the
1989 cost of smoking in California. The object was to "trans-
late into economic terms the human suffering, illness, premature
mortality, and productivity loss caused by smoking."

The study found that the $4.5 billion Californians spent on
cigarettes in 1989 led directly to medical bills of $2.4 billion.
If the added health care costs were added to the price of the
cigarettes, each pack would cost an extra $1.06.

Lost wages for people too sick to work came to $860 mil-
lion. In 1989, 42,207 Californians died from smoking, losing
a total of 643,000 years from their normal life expectancies.
The dollar value of this lost productivity was estimated in the report to be $4.4 billion.

The smoking rate in California is down to 22 percent—25
percent of the men and 19 percent of the women. While the
percentage of smokers is decreasing, ex-smokers will continue
to be stricken with smoking diseases for years to come, creat-
ing grief, pain, and high costs.

❖ ❖

"Tobacco is a filthy weed
That from the devil does proceed;
It drains your purse, it burns your clothes,
And makes a chimney of your nose."

—ANONYMOUS

"I stopped smoking seven years ago, when I was thirty-eight," says Bob E. "And in those years I've done more than I did in the twenty years before. Smoking was conducive to sitting around hour after hour while imagining all the great things I was going to do. They were good as done in my dreams, but in real life I just went to work and watched television.

"After I stopped smoking, I went into action. I'd always liked gardening. I started by putting a very fancy garden in my own yard and designing gardens for friends. Then I took courses in horticulture and landscape design, and now I'm in business. I do pretty well with it, and I love what I do.

"I think if I still smoked, I wouldn't have done any of this. I certainly wouldn't have the energy my business needs. I sleep now like I never slept before. I don't even think about cigarettes."

❖ ❖

"I advise every cigarette victim to have his picture taken every year, and put it aside in a frame in his room, where he can see the gradual, fatal deterioration in himself from year to year. If this does not startle him and bring him to his sense, no amount of preaching will ever do it."

—ORISON SWETT MARDEN,
in Tobacco Under the Searchlight,
by Will H. Brown, 1925

"I am a born-again non-smoker—a confessed sinner

DAY 355

who can now walk into any crowded room without stinking up the joint," wrote Art Buchwald in *The Saturday Evening Post* after recovering from a cigar habit of forty years' duration.

"After I went cold turkey I had to face the prospect of earning a living. I could smoke a cigar without writing, but I couldn't write without smoking a cigar. In the beginning I just stared at the paper. . . . My mind would work in curious ways. I would want to write about the MX missile system, and the only thing that came out was 'Puff the Magic Dragon.'

"Finally, in desperation, I looked up to the heavens and said, 'How long do you expect me to keep this up?' Then the voice came down, 'Try chewing gum.' It worked.

"Well, it's been all uphill since then. After my decompression period I discovered the beautiful world of nonsmoking. My lungs are now getting all the oxygen they so richly deserve, and my brain cells seem to be relieved they don't have to absorb soot from morning until night."

❖   ❖

"I am now a member of that band of brothers and sisters who can walk into a restaurant or get on an airplane and say loudly to the hostess, 'No-smoking section, please!' "
        —ART BUCHWALD,
        The Saturday Evening Post, *July–August 1989*

| DAY 356 | Bad as smoking is for out-
wardly healthy people, it's
worse for sick ones. Smoking depletes the body of nutrients,
slowing or preventing recovery. Malnutrition leads to increased
infections and—in people with breathing problems—
respiratory failure. Smoking not only dulls the appetite, it be-
gets coughing and throat irritations, which make eating harder.

Then there is the negative effect on the immune system, further stacking the cards against the sick person. Smokers are
more prone to pneumonia, which is what often carries off people with chronic diseases.

Wounds heal more slowly (or not at all) in smokers because
of decreased blood flow to the skin and lack of oxygen in the
blood. Increased acid secretions in the digestive system lead to
heartburn and nausea. Smoking also disturbs sleep, particularly in people who suffer from breathing problems.

If you've had any mild illness since you quit smoking, such
as a cold or the flu, you may have noticed that you didn't feel
as lousy as when you were a sick smoker. Smoking makes any
sick person feel worse.

❖ ❖

*"After his return from Winchester . . . he fell into a dangerous
fever, which weakened his mind; he was then also much
troubled with an asthma, or continued short spitting,
but that infirmity he seemed to overcome in good degree
by leaving tobacco, which he had taken somewhat
immoderately."*

—THE LIFE OF SIR HENRY WOTTON, 1670

Marianne Tech's husband died

of lung cancer. "I don't see how anyone could smoke after watching someone die that way," she says. "Over an 18-month period, Larry faded away, shriveling from a man into a corpse. He couldn't eat, he lost his voice, and he had a hell of a time breathing. He was 57 when he died."

Marianne thinks it was passive smoking that killed Larry. He quit smoking 17 years before he was stricken, a period long enough to reduce one's cancer risk to close to normal. But he had for years been in the habit of nursing a beer in a smoke-filled tavern after work, and he died of a type of lung cancer typical in smokers.

Once a heavy smoker herself, Marianne had quit before meeting Larry. At that time, she had been recently divorced and found herself in a world in which she was the only smoker, a social pressure she found conducive to quitting. She now has one longtime friend who smokes, but otherwise finds cigarettes repulsive. "I really don't like being around smokers. If I meet a man who turns out to be a smoker, I lose interest right away."

❖ ❖

OUR KIND: Waiters at Bice Restaurant in Atlanta are not allowed to smoke even on breaks so that they won't offend customers by exuding the smell of cigarettes.

| D A Y   3 5 8 | On this day, a few of you probably still long to smoke.

Occasional urges are altogether natural, and you know how to deal with them. But those of you who are continuously beating back an all but overwhelming lust for cigarettes are suffering more than you should have to.

"There's nothing I like as much as I liked to smoke," says one woman who hasn't smoked for two years. Her hope is that society will change its fickle mind once again and redeem the positive attitude toward smoking it had in her youth.

But we must remark, as did Shakespeare, that "the fault, dear Brutus, is not in our stars, but in ourselves." If you can think of nothing nicer than the nasty practice of smoking, it is not because nothing nicer exists but because you are unable to connect with those other things. This is a mental problem and one common in drug addicts. You might: 1) buy a couple of books on addiction and see what useful suggestions you can find; or 2) find a good shrink. The problem is far from hopeless, but it should be addressed.

❖ ❖

"My vitality is way up since I stopped smoking. When I smoked, I didn't feel like walking or going to the beach. I tried yoga and tai chi, but everything seemed like too much exertion. Everything revolved around cigarettes; it's a whole life-style, a big ball of wax. Since I've quit, I've had huge gaps of time to fill up and much more energy to dispose of."

—BONNIE FOX, *ex-smoker*

Ten years ago, Professor William Weis recommended that

businesses ban smoking. "They would look astonished and say, 'We can't do that.' " Weis, who teaches at the Albers School of Business at Seattle University, now predicts that within a year or two, no workplace will allow smoking.

"With the EPA having officially classified cigarette smoke as a Class A carcinogen, the issue has been taken out of employers' hands, and they will have to subscribe to OSHA [Occupational Safety and Health Administration] standards. They just don't have any choice. Companies which allow smoking will be defenseless in lawsuits. Smoking never should have been allowed in workplaces, considering an employer's common-law duty to provide a healthful environment.

"Financially, the incentive to ban smoking is immense. Employee morale improves. Maintenance costs go down tremendously. Industrial carpeting, lacking cigarette burns, no longer needs changing. Interior window-washing can be reduced from once a month to once a year. The standards for heat and air-conditioning require five times as many air changes when smoking is allowed.

"Once you've eliminated smoking you can go to your fire insurance company and get up to a 35 percent reduction. But not if you have a little back room where people are smoking. Life insurance costs fall too, particularly if the company is self-insuring. And these are just the most tangible savings."

❖ ❖

FACT: The level of carbon monoxide in a smoky, unventilated room can be two to three times the level found at a highly polluted city intersection.

Breath is life to us land animals. When the breath is cut off, for even a few minutes, we die. For millions of people, gasping for breath is the end result of smoking. Practice this meditation in case the idea should ever come to you again that a cigarette might be nice:

❖   ❖

MEDITATION: When I draw a breath, it sails unimpeded down my windpipe, flows on through my two bronchial tubes, divides and proceeds through the little bronchioles, and ends up filling my 600 million teeny air sacs. From the walls of the teeny air sacs, oxygen is absorbed into my bloodstream.

My breath goes in and out pleasantly and unconsciously, unless the tubes or sacs are damaged. If I smoke, a heavy dose of toxins sails down my windpipe along with the air I breathe. These toxins can cause destruction all along the trail. They can create blockages in my main windpipe, clog my bronchial tubes, and dissolve the walls of the tiny air sacs.

I imagine swimming and being caught under water and not knowing if I'll make it to the top in time. That is what living with respiratory disease is like. The thought of death by strangulation is never far away. A cigarette would not be nice.

Your urges to smoke at this point are probably few and far between, but it is likely that someday an occasion will arise when you would rather have a cigarette than live to be old. Nonetheless, even then, you must resist because if you do smoke you will have a greater problem than not living to be old—you will have to quit all over again.

Sandy Rossi hadn't smoked for eight years when she decided to top off her own dinner party with a cigarette. "I don't know what possessed me," she says. "I was being reckless, and I thought—if I thought at all—that a cigarette would only make me sick. Three days later I was smoking several packs a day."

Five years passed before Rossi was able to quit again. "It's not that I liked smoking," she says. "I'm a physical fitness freak and I do aerobics and I knew smoking was nasty and smelly and horrible. This time I had hypnosis, and withdrawal wasn't too bad. I think you can quit ten times and it will be different every time. The last time I felt terribly tense about two minutes out of every hour, but I didn't think about fixing it with a cigarette. I'm very glad to be in control of my life again."

❖ ❖

"After smoking for many years, I finally had enough of the taste, smell, and the look. It was no longer cool for an 80s lady to be engulfed in a cloud of smoke."

K. T. OSLIN, *singer, ex-smoker*

| D A Y 3 6 2 | Ralph Howard Hill, who spent a long time quitting, believes

that the physical addiction to cigarettes takes years to dissipate. "When you first quit, you think of a cigarette every ten seconds. Then every minute. Then a few times a day. Even after five or eight years, I used to feel a powerful urge about once a year. It was as strong as ever, for about two minutes."

Hill says that whenever he did relapse it was out of a feeling of helplessness. "It would be when I felt I couldn't cope, couldn't control my destiny. Why bother fighting? Smoking is an act of despair."

Hill had organized his quitting (see Day 292) around numerous strategies and substitutions, such as sucking on a baby bottle. "Having all these things to throw at smoking made me feel not helpless." When years later, the urge to smoke—charged by that old feeling of helplessness—would overtake him, he'd resurrect a quitting technique or two.

Ten years after his last cigarette, the urge to smoke for Hill finally decamped. After 17 years, he can say, "I can't imagine ever wanting a cigarette again. The addiction is finally gone. People should realize that the urge gives up eventually, but it can take a lot longer than they expect."

❖ ❖

DAY'S TIP: Make a list of situations that could make you want to smoke and list alternatives to smoking for each one. Review the list often enough so that when the moment comes, your response will be automatic.

Doctors observed in the 1930s that most of their lung cancer patients were smokers. The tobacco industry denied a connection. Since then, millions of dogs, monkeys, chickens, chimpanzees, guinea pigs, rabbits, cats, rats, and mice have died miserably in laboratories in efforts to prove or disprove connections between smoking and disease. In the case of lung cancer, the slaughter has been a setback for human health. Animals don't get human types of lung cancer so the experiments supported the tobacco industry position.

Today, thousands of animals are still writhing in cages while hooked up to smoking machines. The tobacco industry uses cigarette dollars to fund animal "research," and this "research" then clouds the results of the equally gruesome experiments funded with tax dollars. The psychologists pump nicotine into thousands more defenseless animals to study the course of nicotine addiction. Thanks to them, we can now all be sure that nicotine is addictive!

We have had scientific evidence since the 17th century, when physicians first autopsied smokers and saw their black lungs, that smoking is no good. If everyone stopped smoking tomorrow, tobacco companies would have no money for tobacco research and the rest of the scientific community would have no excuse for it.

❖ ❖

"The simple and unfortunate fact is that scientists do not know the cause or causes of the chronic diseases reported to be associated with smoking. The answers ... can only be determined through much more scientific research."
—Jo F. Spach, R.J. Reynolds Tobacco Co.,
letter to a fifth-grade class, dated January 11, 1990

| D A Y   3 6 4 | Enough about smoking. You don't want to get cancer? You want to be jaunty at 100? Eat your vegetables. Fresh fruits and vegetables protect our species from oxidative damage, the cause of much bodily breakdown and cancer. Cigarette smoke is one of the avoidable oxidants, but life is full of others. Consequently, we must consume our antioxidants—five to nine fruits and vegetables a day.

"If we could get everybody to stop smoking and eat five fruits and vegetables a day, I think we would have a very substantial impact on public health," says Dr. Gladys Block, a Berkeley epidemiologist. "It's clear from population studies that fruits and vegetables are protective against some cancers, and probably against some other diseases too."

There is strong evidence that vitamin C, vitamin E, and beta carotene (a vitaminlike nutrient) protect against cancers of the esophagus, larynx, mouth, and most particularly, lung. As you, even after a year of not smoking, are still at high risk from these cancers, you would be very smart go to the market and fill your cart with citrus fruits, broccoli, strawberries, cauliflower, peppers, brussel sprouts, spinach, collard greens, and kale. And, of course, you surely already know to substitute meat and dairy with beans and grains—but that's another subject.

❖ ❖

"Evolutionarily we ate vastly more fruits and vegetables than we do now. And we didn't smoke."
—GLADYS BLOCK, *epidemiologist, University of California*

Of those who set sail without cigarettes a year ago, 27 percent of you are still on board.

You are the happy ones. Nobody ever regrets quitting smoking. The author of this book recalls with horror her office in days of yore, a full ashtray tilted precariously on a pile of books, the air heavy with smoke, her fingers yellow. She was generally in a bad mood. Looking back, it seems as if her life had not quite begun.

Tomorrow you celebrate. A year is a long time not to smoke, although in some ways it's just a beginning. Physically, you've recuperated immensely, but habits die hard, and psychological change is slow. If you sometimes still feel shaky, it's not because you are fated to ever be so. Learning to survive without cigarettes is a long-term undertaking. Whatever strides you've made in the past 365 days will be magnified in the years to come—as long as you don't smoke.

Despite your achievement, the time has not come to let down your guard. One-third of former smokers relapse after a year; the surgeon general will not classify you as a confirmed nonsmoker for yet another year. The relapse curve for former smokers never evens out altogether. But for most of us, the passage of years serves to wipe out any lingering desire to smoke. Let us all fervently hope that in a few more years, the custom of smoking will have faded from civilization altogether.

❖   ❖

"In its short and nasty history, cigarette smoking has produced merely bogus pleasure and incalculable harm."
—WILLIAM STYRON, **The Nation**, *March 7, 1987*